ZEN MAMAS

Teresa Palmer and Sarah Wright Olsen are the founders of the internationally popular blog *Your Zen Mama*, an online destination for parents that offers open, reassuring and inspiring advice on every step of the parenting journey.

Teresa is a mother of three, Bodhi, Forest and Poet, and stepmother to Isaac. She has starred in many major films, including Mel Gibson's *Hacksaw Ridge*, for which she received an AACTA nomination for best supporting actress, and *Ride Like a Girl*, the biopic of trailblazing Melbourne Cup winner Michelle Payne. She is currently playing the starring role in Sky series *A Discovery of Witches* while running the plant-based wellness brand Lovewell, which she co-founded with Chrissy Duigan. Teresa splits her time between homes in Adelaide and the Hollywood Hills.

Sarah is a mother of two, Esmé and Wyatt. An actor living in Los Angeles, Sarah has starred in many TV shows and movies including *Mad Men*, *Parks and Recreation*, *The House Bunny* and opposite Tom Cruise in *American Made*. She is currently working on a show for Netflix called *Spinning Out*. Sarah is also the co-owner of a plant-based organic mummy/baby skincare line, Bāeo.

yourzenmama.com

Dedicated to our children,
Wyatt, Bodhi, Esmé, Forest, Poet & Isaac.

In loving memory of
Robert L Wright and Dora Sanders.

ZEN MAMAS

TERESA PALMER SARAH WRIGHT OLSEN

CONTENTS

INTRODUCTION

Ahhh, Zen. Not a word that springs to mind for most parents! That elusive state of being seems to exist only in the dreamiest versions of ourselves. So, what exactly is 'Zen'? And what images are conjured up when you hear this word?

Do you see a group of serene people dressed in white, bathed in the hue of gentle sunshine with their hands held together in prayer, melodically omming to the same note? Do you imagine children frolicking through fields of poppies as their mothers pick berries and weave flower crowns to lay upon their heads? Does living a Zen life sound like some hokey LA thing where communes of patchouli-scented vegans brew their own kombucha and 'create space' to process their emotions? Where a lush willow-filled forest provides the backdrop to an orgasmic birth, followed by a gentle landing in a postpartum bed of rose petals?

Despite what Instagram might have you believe, this beautiful yet somewhat puke-inducing bubble of bliss doesn't actually exist. Any seemingly perfect snapshots like these are just small snippets from people's lives (or marketing campaigns), and not at all reflective of the daily grind taking place in all kinds of households all over the world. So how has the word Zen become so wildly misused and misunderstood?

In its purest form, the word Zen comes from a Mahayana Buddhist movement, a centuries-old practice focusing on meditation as a way of achieving enlightenment. Over the years the term Zen has become synonymous with feelings of presence, acceptance, self-realisation, being at peace and finding balance. This vast definition of Zen means the philosophy can resonate with everyone. It's flexible and inclusive. To us, Zen is about working towards a feeling of alignment, balance and self-care, setting us up for more positive, fulfilling and grounding relationships with ourselves, our children and those around us. We find that when we are doing the work to live more consciously, we are less triggered by the array of life's colours, some more challenging than others.

So, what's our reality as 'Zen mamas' – and how Zen is it really? Well, a lot of the time it's messy homes, frazzled parents, crazy kids, dirty nappies, fighting siblings, piles of washing, rubbish-filled cars, late school drop-offs, forgotten everythings, last-minute homework, TV binges, plastic toys, tantrums, all the ice-creams one can possibly find and the array of other chaos and corner-cutting that comes with having kids. Phew!

But then, on the flip side, there's also sleeping babies, blissful breastfeeding, lazy beach days, camping adventures, giggle fits, nature play, homemade food, meditation, kids' yoga and happy, loving, card-making, conscious-minded children. With peaceful mamas, happy papas and those pinch-me-I'm-dreaming moments . . .

Let's be honest: motherhood doesn't exist in the highlights reel of life, but finding a fleeting semblance of calm, acceptance and presence among the inevitable pandemonium is what we try to do. We try to embrace the real-ness, the not-going-to-plan-ness and the imperfect-ness of our picture. Being Zen(ish) is what we call it – and it's the *ish* that we endorse!

When we started our blog, *Your Zen Mama*, in 2014, we were both young mothers looking to unite a community of women from all over the world. We wanted a place to share our stories and to learn from each other – a positive platform for uplifting, encouraging, supporting and commiserating with one another on the remarkable and challenging experience that is parenthood. The blog's growth and success suggests that we weren't the only ones looking for this kind of community.

We are now two mamas with six children between us: Sarah is mama to 6-year-old son Wyatt and 3-year-old daughter Esmé. Teresa is mama to 6-year-old son Bodhi, 3-year-old son Forest and 1-year-old daughter Poet; and also has a 12-year-old stepson, Isaac. In our non-existent free time we run two businesses between us, Bāeo and Lovewell, act in TV shows and movies, and care deeply about sustainability, animal rights, wellness, plant-based living, mindfulness, natural parenting and true crime podcasts! (The *ish*, remember?!)

We believe that there is no perfect version of motherhood, no One Size Fits All – we are all unique and individual. We're not here to preach that one way of doing things is better than another. Instead, we are here to share some of the knowledge we have collected over the years from our inspiring Zen Mama community, from our mentors and from being in the trenches of motherhood ourselves. We've found that this generosity of sharing information and advice can make a huge difference to one's journey through motherhood, so writing this book is our way of giving back and saying thanks to every person who's shared their knowledge with us in the past.

In this book we'll talk about the magical myths surrounding conception, birth stories, our postpartum experiences, the first few years, and loss and love. We'll share our hopes for the future, what we are doing to lay the foundations for our families, how we're trying to make our planetary footprints smaller, and why the women in our lives are so incredibly important. We want to give you as much as we possibly can so you can take what works for you and make your own decisions. We want to help you find that level of peace and joy that comes from letting go and creating your own version of a Zen life.

So, strap on your yoga pants and let's dive in!

PREGNANCY PREP

ONE

So you're scrolling through Instagram one day, getting double-tap happy, when you notice that your feed feels a little different. Where usually you'd be commenting on yummy food, feminist quotes and gorgeous landscapes, suddenly you're seeing multiple pics of freckled kids, pregnant bellies and babies.

Days later, you're strolling down the street. You hear a noise, look round and PRAMS. Everywhere. Perplexed, you start counting them. *Seventeen* prams. You feel like Jim Carrey in *The Truman Show*. *Is everyone in on a plot about me getting knocked up?* Just then a fleet of mini-vans drives by with that token yellow 'Baby on Board' sign hanging in the back window of every one. You whip out your phone to google *are we in a baby boom?* Suddenly, right on cue, a baby locks eyes with you. As the world slows, your body melts into your uterus. *Oh yeah, my uterus*, you think to yourself, subconsciously touching your tummy as you drift into a daydream about having your own little lump of adorableness.

This is called baby fever, and, although it's not a medical term, generations of women can attest to its existence. Some of us get it young (including the both of us), others a little older. Some don't experience it until after their baby is born, and some not at all. But if you come down with this infamous 'fever', it can seem almost impossible to think of anything else.

So, we've established that you want to get pregnant. Whether you have a partner, a donor, a surrogate or you just want to prepare yourself for the future, we're going to start from the beginning.

Bringing a baby into this world is a life-changing experience, and one that can bring up lots of emotions, even before you've embarked on the journey itself. You may not feel ready for a very long time, and then out of the blue it becomes all you can think about. For us, all the things that changed – some hard, some really beautiful – brought us into this new and amazing stage of life. It's not always easy, but its challenges have taught us some of the most profound lessons we could ever learn. What motherhood is for you is your own unique story. Through any adventure in life we have the opportunity to learn, grow and find out more about ourselves. This evolution is our own. We get to decide how we see motherhood. We shape how we feel, and we can choose to follow our knowing feeling, the one deep inside of us that we will come to know as our 'mama instinct'. With research comes knowledge, and if we align that knowledge with intuition, we can meet the peaks and valleys of our mothering journey from an informed place.

IS NOW THE RIGHT TIME?

This is an important question to ask yourself, even though there isn't always a clear-cut answer. Trying to 'plan' a baby in a chuck-it-in-the-old-Google-Calendar kinda way isn't actually practical – nor does it work! Babies are utterly unpredictable. It's almost impossible to pencil in the creation of a new life. Often we create conditions around it, saying things like, 'Once I get that promotion', or 'Next year when we have a bit more in our savings', or 'In a few months we'll start trying, then hopefully our baby will be born on 15 March, on my mother's birthday. I'll name her Eleanor after her great-grandmother and she'll be a Pisces!' Though this sounds lovely and neat in theory, the reality is that precision is a rarity. Life brings unexpected challenges and transitions that could throw baby plans out the window. Often there's no definitive answer as to when the perfect time is, and sometimes we will be surprised with baby news when we least expect it.

We often hear parents being quick to lay on the doomsday negativity when discussing raising kids. Well-intentioned comments aimed at 'giving you a heads up' can make motherhood sound like years of self-inflicted torture that you don't *ever* fancy signing up to – whether it's 'Well, have fun now because you will NEVER sleep again!' or 'Take those trips while you can, cause you'll be under house arrest until your kid is five!' Don't let someone else's experience dictate how you feel about yours. You don't want to take on that energy. Embarking on the motherhood journey is daunting as it is, so keep your space sacred and steer clear of those who like to wreak havoc with their fear-inducing stories!

LET'S TALK ABOUT BABIES

Acknowledging that you may never feel *fully* ready to have a baby, the most important thing you can do is sit down with your partner and have an open and candid conversation about raising children and what that might look like for you both. Are you on the same page? If the answer to that question is yes, then great. If it feels like you are out of sync, it may be a good idea to ask some more questions, or put a pin in the 'starting a family' conversation.

Sarah: I always wanted to have kids. Even from a very young age I remember loving babies and the idea of motherhood. When I fell in love with my husband, Eric, I talked about our future all the time. I let him know early on that I wanted a family, and he let me know that we were not ready. When we met I was twenty-two and he was twenty-eight, and we waited six years to get married and start trying for a baby. I am so grateful we waited. I can't imagine myself as a mother in my early twenties, so I am grateful that we were not in sync at the time. I knew things were changing when Eric seemed to get excited when we would talk about having a baby. We talked about our philosophies on raising kids. We spoke about what we would name our babies one day. I think we talked about babies for a whole year before we started trying. We were in the middle of redoing a home, we had just been married, and after a couple of months of trying, we found out we were pregnant – the same week we moved into our new house.

HOW TO BEGIN

Clear communication is important in any relationship, but it can be tricky to know how to raise the subject of having a baby. If you're not the type to grab a glass of red wine and casually drop 'So, my ovaries are wondering if your balls are on the same page?', a good alternative might be 'Where do you see us in five years?' If a baby is not in the picture, don't panic – just find out why. You may be ready but your partner may feel different, and that is okay. Talking through any concerns, worries or fears together can actually help you understand each other and feel united in your next steps. It is important to let your partner know how you feel, but always do so from a loving and open-minded place, as these are such delicate topics (and body parts!).

Most importantly, you'll ideally be in a situation that feels supportive and loving before bringing new life into the world. We call that responsible conception! A baby doesn't fix something that's broken, nor does it exist in those fairytale Instagram snapshots we see on the reg. Having a baby is hard work, so check your emotional state and your mental health and evaluate your partnership dynamic *first*. If those important things are feeling balanced, then you have the foundation you need to begin a family.

YOUR LIVING SITUATION

So let's say you have the 'foundation' down: you've agreed you both want to start trying and you're in a situation that feels encouraging and positive. Now what do you focus on addressing? We suggest thinking carefully about the shape of your life to determine if it's really conducive to adding a new, little but fierce family member. Here are some important things to think about and discuss.

- **Home:** Is your current home the perfect fit for a family, or will you need to move? Is there enough space? Do you have access to things like healthcare and childcare nearby?

- **Finances:** Cash flow is a big thing. If you're struggling to stay afloat financially now, then you either need to change aspects of your lifestyle to create room for a baby, or wait until things have stabilised. If you want a clearer idea of your finances you can speak to a financial advisor and plan a budget. This will give you a better understanding of what you need to cover the cost of a family. According to the Australian Institute of Family Studies, a first child costs between $3000 and $13 000 in the first year alone. We're not saying this to scare you, but it may make for a less stressful pregnancy if you have some simple plans in place.

- **Work:** What does your work – yours and that of your partner – offer in terms of maternity leave or paternity leave? Is it paid or unpaid? Will either of you need to change jobs before or after having your baby?

- **Community/family support:** Think about your support network (family, friends, paid carers) – who will you be able to lean on when you need help, advice and company?

☆ **Personal goals:** Are there any really pressing things that either of you wish to achieve in your own lives, like travelling, or living in that tiny Paris apartment eating baguettes and cheese every day? Is there anything you feel must be in place before taking on such a huge responsibility? (Side note: We travel everywhere with our babies and kids and we love it, so don't assume that having a baby puts a halt on travel dreams.)

Being able to discuss these things with your partner will help you feel like you're working towards a common goal, high-fiving your teammate along the way. Pregnancy, birth and beyond is all about camaraderie, and these initial conversations are a crucial first step.

Teresa: Mark and I certainly didn't wait till the 'right' time. We were pregnant within eight months of dating! But funnily enough we were trying for a baby. I look back now and think 'boy did we get lucky' – that could've gone pear shaped real quick! We really hardly knew each other, but there was a feeling, the knowing one we talked about earlier. We talked about having a baby at length. He knew that being a mother was my number one dream in life, and he had a similar sentiment about being a father. I saw how beautiful he was with his son, Isaac, and given that he had been around the fatherhood block once before, the decision to have more kids was an effortless one – so we went for it!

PREPARING YOUR HEALTH FOR PREGNANCY

Physical and mental health is important for everyone, but it is especially important when you are trying to conceive. Before you start trying to conceive, schedule an appointment with your doctor or find a midwife through recommendations – or do a good ol' google search for licensed midwives in your area. Meeting midwives or doctors is like dating: it's all about finding the right person, someone you trust and feel aligned with. What does that mean exactly? Well, all care providers are different. In our experience, some obstetricians are very personable and will spend time with you answering questions, whereas others move very quickly and you can feel a bit bulldozed when trying to figure out your options. With midwives, you will often spend a lot more dedicated time learning about nutrition, going over your options and doing detailed check-ups – you may feel as if you are their only client. It's a very personal and unique experience, so it is important to find the care provider who is right for you. Hospital midwives generally only meet up with you once you're pregnant; however, many home birth midwives will happily meet a couple who are about to embark on their pregnancy journey. Let your care provider know that you and your partner are thinking about getting pregnant and ask for advice on what the next steps might be. You should have an updated pap smear, and your care provider will be able to give you instructions according to what birth control you might be taking.

Sarah: I had both a midwife and an obstetrician. My first obstetrician was cold and I felt like I needed to reexplain who I was every single visit. At four months pregnant I decided to swap to a home birth with a midwife, and the care I received from her was incredible: she'd spend an hour with me every visit, talking about my feelings surrounding birth, my goals, nutrition and my family. I knew I wanted a hospital birth the second time around (my first baby was very large!), and I sought out Dr Goldberg based on amazing stories from his patients. He'd spend more time with me than he probably could spare, discussing everything from the size of my babies to how my father was sick and dying while I was pregnant. He stayed in the room the entire two hours I was in labour with Esmé and was a wonderful support.

PRE-PREGNANCY SUPPLEMENTS

Suggestions on what you should take before trying to conceive may vary according to your blood work and your diet, but most care providers will suggest that you start taking folate (folic acid), prenatal vitamins and DHA. That's right, they'll have you start taking pregnancy supplements before you're pregnant. This sounded weird to us too, but there are good reasons for doing so.

FOLATE: WHAT THE PROFESSIONALS SAY

Folate is a naturally occurring vitamin found in foods such as green leafy vegetables, legumes, nuts and eggs. Folic acid is the form that is added to foods like bread, cereals or supplements. The Centers for Disease Control and Prevention (CDC) and the American College of Obstetricians and Gynecologists (ACOG) suggest that all women of reproductive age start taking folate even if they are not planning a pregnancy, because almost half of all pregnancies are unplanned. Essentially, folate is so important that you should take it *just in case* you get pregnant, and continue to do so once you are.

According to the CDC, 'All women of reproductive age should get 400 micrograms of folic acid each day, in addition to consuming food with folate from a varied diet, to help prevent neural tube defects (NTDs). NTDs are major birth defects of the baby's brain (anencephaly) and spine (spina bifida).' Current dietary guidelines from the ACOG recommend that pregnant women get at least 600 micrograms of folic acid daily from all sources – that is, from supplements and food combined. You can get folate, the food-based form of folic acid, from foods such as dark leafy greens, lentils, nuts, beans and eggs, but it can be hard to get enough from what you eat unless you are eating fortified food.

- fruit (avocado, grapefruit, orange)
- eggs
- nuts
- vegetables (broccoli, Brussels sprouts, cabbage, cauliflower, English spinach, green beans, lettuce, mushrooms, parsnip, sweet corn, zucchini)
- legumes (chickpeas, soya beans, lima beans, red kidney beans, lentils, haricot beans)
- juices (many apple and orange juices)

FOODS FORTIFIED WITH FOLIC ACID

- breakfast cereal
- cornmeal
- products made from corn masa (corn chips, taco shells)
- flour
- pasta
- white rice

WHAT SHOULD I EAT?

We suggest getting your body ready for pregnancy by eating healthy, balanced meals full of nutrients and vitamins that will support the growth of new life. Australian clinical nutritionist Maria Harpas agrees: 'For those of you who are not yet pregnant,' she says, 'there is never a time that is more important to pay attention to what you are doing to your body than the months before conceiving. You want to prime and prepare your body to host, nourish and grow another human being. Eating and sleeping well, avoiding environmental chemicals, exercising and reducing stressors are key. Not only do we want our children to be healthy, we want to feel good while this is happening, so we can better serve our new bubs and ourselves.'

So, cut out those foods you know aren't good for you – chances are, they won't be good for your developing baby, either. This doesn't mean you have to totally deprive yourself of sweets or that bag of chips you're craving, but you should listen to your midwife or doctor and consider their suggestions. Whatever your fitness level, it is incredibly important to make a plan with your care provider to help you reach optimum health. Remember, we all have our own personal health journeys, so while we're offering our suggestions here, your doctor is your key partner in figuring out the best diet for you and your baby.

SOME BASIC TIPS FOR HEALTHIER EATING

When trying to eat healthier, it can be hard to know where to start. Here are a few rules of thumb that we follow:

- Eat balanced meals made with organic foods.
- Cut back on packaged, processed foods.
- Avoid corn syrup.
- Make superfood smoothies.

And when time just isn't on your side, rather than reaching for something processed or prepared, try one of these quick or instant alternatives.

FIVE-MINUTE SNACKS TO MAKE AT HOME

- Almond butter on rice cakes with sliced banana
- Smashed avo on toast with lime juice, pepper and salt
- Hummus on seeded crackers with sliced cucumber

- Coconut yoghurt with a handful of berries and cinnamon
- Tahini on toast with sliced apple and a drizzle of honey

OUR GO-TO STORE-BOUGHT SNACKS
FOR NUTRITION ON THE RUN

- Organic punnet of blueberries or raspberries
- Raw protein or muesli bars (watch out for the sugars)
- Chia pods
- Any type of raw nuts
- Baby carrots and hummus
- Green smoothies

HEALTH AND MOVEMENT

Exercise is important for both you and your future fetus. We're not saying you need to become a triathlete, but incorporating movement into your routine can have a lot of benefits for fertility and pregnancy. Some of these benefits are:

- Stress relief
- Improved circulation and blood flow
- Moving meditation
- Dedicated time with you and your partner, e.g. going for a walk together

A recent study also found that moderate exercise may increase a woman's chances of falling pregnant. Dr Gabriela Mena Ribadeneira, from the University of Queensland's School of Human Movement and Nutrition Sciences, analysed research on reproductive health and exercise from the last two decades. She reported that, 'When physical activity was compared with standard fertility treatments, such as IVF or ovulation induction, there was no difference in pregnancy rates and live births between women exercising and those undertaking fertility treatments.[1] This suggests that physical activity may be as effective as commonly used fertility treatments, and could be an affordable and feasible alternative or complementary therapy to these very expensive treatments.' The study also found higher pregnancy and live birth rates for women who were physically active than women who were undergoing fertility treatments or were not undertaking exercise. No specific exercise was quoted as being more effective than another.

We both used the same midwife, Davi Kaur Khalsa, CNM, NP, MSN, for our first babies and one of the first things she did, as she handed us a booklet filled with empty pages to use as a food journal, was to impart a wealth of information on the importance of moving our bodies. This doesn't just apply to pre-pregnancy but throughout pregnancy too. Davi also stressed the power of utilising movement in birth. She told us that if we were serious about having home births (which we were), we should be walking eight kilometres a day – and the Royal Women's Hospital advises that walking 10 000 steps per day or exercising for 150 minutes over the course of a week will prepare you physically for labour. This is because you need stamina to get through a potentially long birth. You could be walking, standing or squatting for hours during your labour, and you will need your strength to push through and keep going. Conditioning your body while pregnant by walking is an amazing way to keep your body moving. Eight kilometres sounded like a lot, but we were up for the challenge – though in reality, trying to walk that distance becomes a daily commitment of more than two hours! Disclaimer: Teresa *did not* walk eight kilometres a day, maybe not even once. Sarah, on the other hand, was a more dedicated student and managed between three and five miles a day, about five days a week.

Does this mean you have to walk that much? No, but don't wait until you are pregnant to start incorporating movement into your routine. Get these habits in place beforehand to ensure you can maintain a healthy lifestyle while pregnant. Whether it's yoga, the gym or your favourite dance class, having your exercise or movement routine sorted will mean there's one less thing to think about when other aspects of your life and body start to change!

SEX

So, you've seen the doctor, you're eating well and taking vitamins, and you're hiking a bit during the week or maybe grabbing a yoga class when you have a chance. Next is the fun part, the part people typically consider being *first* in this equation: sex.

It's funny how much time you spend trying *not* to get pregnant, then the moment you feel ready, it's like 'How does this work? Is there a trick?' Suddenly that three-letter word that once felt naughty, exciting, daunting, romantic or just plain fun has a little more attached to it.

Perhaps a couple of months pass, doubt creeps in and you turn to your friends, asking for suggestions. Is it true that missionary style is the best way to get pregnant? Does it work better if the man and woman orgasm at the same time? (So romantic!) Can you get pregnant if you were drinking the night you had sex? (One thousand per cent yes!) Didn't someone say to do a back bend or prop your bum up with a pillow for twenty fully annoying minutes before running to the bathroom to pee? (Yep, we totally tried this.)

> **Teresa:** No joke, one night post-lounge room shenanigans Mark carried me down the stairs UPSIDE DOWN just so that we didn't have any 'spillage'. That was not the month we got pregnant . . .

SEX AND PREGNANCY: WHAT THE PROFESSIONALS SAY

As for how often, the general advice is that vaginal sexual intercourse every two to three days optimises your chances of pregnancy. But of course your chances of conceiving will increase if you pay attention to your cycle and know when you are ovulating.

Teresa: I tried the every other day method for five months and didn't get pregnant. I then decided to up the ante (poor Mark) and we did it TWICE a day, a.m. and p.m., every day during my fertile period (I used an ovulation predication calculator to pinpoint our mega action week). And boom: I was pregnant.

Sarah: We tried for a couple months without thinking about it, but then I became impatient. I had read about the every other day method, and used an ovulation prediction kit. This took a couple more months, but it finally worked.

There are no current studies to tell us whether certain positions make it easier to get pregnant, but the two common positions that people talk about are missionary and doggie style. The reason these two positions are talked about anecdotally is because penetration is deeper and closer to the cervix, so sperm have a shorter distance to travel. While there isn't sufficient scientific evidence for this, from what we have read, you want to avoid the sperm running out of you post-sex – so we've applied our own logic here!

FERTILITY

Sarah: Pre-babies, I thought you simply decide to get pregnant, stop wearing condoms or taking birth control, have lots of sex and then you get pregnant. Easy!

'Fertility' is a word that seems to come up a lot these days, often followed by the word 'infertility'. Infertility is defined as the inability to conceive a pregnancy after twelve months of unprotected sex. It affects about one in six Australian couples of reproductive age. For us and the women in our lives, the moment we feel ready to try for pregnancy, doubt creeps in and our minds race off to some extreme dystopian world similar to *The Handmaid's Tale*, where women are less and less fertile – and we suddenly fear this will be our story, too. But not being able to get pregnant right away does *not* mean you are infertile. So many things have to go right for you to conceive, it is truly a miracle that it happens! If there is an issue, it could be with your partner, your cycle, the amount of stress in your life, or your timing.

IT'S ALL ABOUT TIMING

There are a few different ways to track ovulation during your cycle. Doing this can improve your chances of having sex at the perfect moment for operation egg drop. Some tracking methods are easier than others, but all have been proven effective.

1. OVULATION PREDICTOR

Some women like to track their ovulation with an ovulation predictor kit. You can pick one up at the chemist, in the same section where you buy pregnancy tests. This isn't 100 per cent accurate – you can get false readings on these things – but if it works for you it can be a super handy tool. That beeping smiley face can be your best pal in a month of tracking ovulation.

> **Teresa:** I used Clearblue Advanced ovulation prediction tests with my first two pregnancies. I have always ovulated at different times in my cycle, so finding my fertile period cut down the months it took for us to get pregnant each time. I highly recommend!

There are also apps for ovulation prediction – you put in very minimal information to start tracking your periods and changes in your body and before you know it you have a fully documented calendar of days you had sex, when you were supposed to start your period and an estimate of ovulation. One app we are loving right now is called Flo.

> **Sarah:** When I tried to conceive my first baby it took me a few months to realise I ovulated much earlier than I thought. Typically we're told that ovulation happens on around day 12 of our cycle, but I was actually ovulating on day 9. We would miss our window entirely! That's why I loved using an ovulation cycle app. With the calendar you can make notes, heart the days when you have sex and track changes in your mood, cramps and cervical mucus. This felt much more efficient to me and worked for both of my pregnancies.

2. CHECK YOUR TEMPERATURE

You can also monitor your basal core temperature to help plan when to try to conceive. According to Planned Parenthood, 'Your body temperature naturally changes a tiny bit throughout your menstrual cycle. It's lower in the first part of your cycle, and then rises when you ovulate.' Before ovulation a woman's basal body temperature averages between 36.1°C and 36.4°C. After ovulation, it rises to 36.4°C to 37°C. To use the temperature method, you must take your temperature the same way every single day, and record it on a fertility awareness chart.

You can find fertility awareness charts at the Family Planning organisation in your state or online, or you can ask a nurse or care provider. There are even devices like the Daysy Fertility Tracker (on the pricier side) or basal body thermometers (you can get them starting at $15) that will monitor your basal core temperature and help you get to know your cycle. You have to take your temperature the moment you wake up to get an accurate reading, so make sure you follow the directions.

3. CHECK YOUR MUCUS

DISCLAIMER: We are going to use words like vagina, discharge and mucus, so if this kind of language makes you queasy, grab some ginger ale so we can talk about your insides.

The hormones that control your menstrual cycle produce a mucus from your cervix called cervical mucus (CM). You can chart the changes in your mucus to gain a better understanding of the different stages it goes through, as these can help you predict ovulation. Pregnancy and birth have never been described as 'cookie cutter' or a 'clean and easy process' – you will come to know your body in a whole new light! You will also be more in tune with what is happening inside you. We were blown away by our bodies, what they are capable of and how they work to grow life.

It's never too early to get comfortable and explore your vagina. Put your fingers inside and get to know what you feel like. A lot of women aren't really sure of the location of their cervix, which is totally normal – unless you are looking at an anatomy book and 'exploring' at the same time, it's hard to know the exact location. Don't be afraid to ask your doctor/midwife to show you where it is when they are examining you.

There are a few different ways to check your CM. In general, we ladies have discharge. Before you pee, wipe your vagina and check the colour and texture of the discharge. Look at the colour and texture in your underwear. Put clean fingers inside your vagina and check the colour and texture on your fingers by rubbing

17

your index finger and thumb together. Start tracking your CM the day after your period ends and note what you see: dry, sticky, creamy, watery, etc.

If your cycle is long you may have dry days, and if your CM is dry, chances are you're not ovulating. Your body will start making mucus when an egg starts to ripen before ovulation. At this point the mucus will be sticky, tacky and yellow or white in colour. Your most fertile days (possibly up to four days) will be when your CM is slippery and clear and can be stretchy between your fingers. This is often described as the egg white cervical mucus, because it resembles raw egg whites. This will be the best time to have sex, because your CM is the most sperm-friendly and gives those swimmers the 'lube' they need to reach the egg. Then your CM will go back to being cloudy, white or yellow and could be followed by some dry days before your period begins again. If you find you have a lot of dry days leading up to ovulation, make sure you are getting enough hydration. Taking antihistamines can also inhibit mucus production.

Every cycle is different, so we can't tell you exactly when this will all occur. Getting familiar with your body and keeping track of what you see will give you a better understanding of what stage you are in and when you are likely to conceive.

WHEN IS BEST TO TAKE THAT TEST?

Most of the women we know who are trying to conceive have a stash of pregnancy tests under their sink, ready to go. The at-home early predictor pregnancy tests are actually very accurate, and can predict up to six days ahead of your next cycle. The second line may be very light, but that doesn't mean you are any less pregnant, it just means the pregnancy hormone, human chorionic gonadotropin (HCG), isn't as strong yet. Feel free to take the test ahead of time, but waiting until the day you are supposed to start your period may save you some of those very expensive pregnancy tests. Take into consideration when you ovulate. If you ovulate late, you may not be able to see a positive test six days early because the HCG will not show up yet.

Teresa: I am a chronic pee-on-a-stick-er. If you're at all familiar with the online trying-to-conceive lingo you'd know that DPO stands for 'days past ovulation'. It typically takes around a week, give or take, for those fertilised eggs to implant, and the moment the implantation occurs your HCG level will start to rise. I typically start testing from 9DPO (nine days past ovulation)! With Bodhi I got a BFP (Big Fat Positive) at 9DPO, with Forest my first BFP was at 10DPO, and with Poet I had the sliiiiightest hint of a BFP at 8DPO, although that's very early. I have zero patience, but if I had more I'd make myself wait until at least 11DPO before whipping out a pregnancy test, just to save disappointment. I'd also suggest not using a digital test until after your missed period, as you could get a false negative. Try one of the super sensitive pregnancy tests, like the early detection First Response test with the two pink lines. It's exciting to watch the line get darker day by day (or in my obsessive case, 12 hours by 12 hours!).

BOOSTING YOUR FERTILITY

After about six months of trying with no luck, some women are ready to look for help, and are beginning to ask, 'Is there more I could be doing?' The answer is actually yes.

DR ELLIOT BERLIN, DC — AWARD-WINNING PRENATAL CHIROPRACTOR, CHILDBIRTH EDUCATOR AND LABOUR SUPPORT BODYWORKER

I am a chiropractor and bodyworker and my wife, Alyssa, is a psychologist. We were in our twenties when we started trying to have our first baby. After a year of trying without conceiving, we were very concerned and sought medical advice. We then spent the next couple of years enduring unsuccessful medical testing and treatments that were physically, emotionally and financially gruelling. The doctors were baffled, too, and told us that we'd likely never conceive.

We took a break for some time to heal and started going on more dates. We began to exercise regularly, eat better and try out stuff like yoga, meditation and Chinese medicine (we come from pretty medical backgrounds where these things are a bit fru fru). Feeling better inside and out, we were almost ready to consider other routes to parenthood when, to our ecstatic surprise, we found out we were pregnant (mostly Alyssa). Then, two years later, it happened again. And then again two more times after that. When it rains it pours! Our joint prenatal, postpartum and paediatric practice evolved from there – our original focus on improving overall health with an eye on boosting natural fertility appealed to newly pregnant clients who wanted to continue to see us for prenatal wellness care.

The nervous system controls the function of every cell and organ within the body. For many of us, the nervous system leans towards 'fight or flight' mode even when we are not in any apparent external danger. Sometimes those stimuli come from stressors – financial, relationship, work, political – all of which create elements of anxiety and fear. Processing and managing these internal stressors through certain modalities can help shift our autonomic nervous system into a more relaxed and, perhaps, more fertile mode of operation. The hormonal system plays a major role in fertility and reproduction as well, and other modalities exist to help regulate that too.

There are many factors that could delay or prevent conception or interfere with the body's ability to nurture or sustain a healthy pregnancy, and it is not abnormal for it to take several cycles to conceive; about 80 per cent of people trying succeed within six months. If you're not within that 80 per cent, here are some modalities to consider alongside traditional medical investigation as you look to prepare your mind and body for a healthy conception, pregnancy, birth and transition to parenthood. We used these three modalities ourselves and now practise them on our clients – they're relevant to both potential parents, as it takes two to tango!

CHIROPRACTIC

While chiropractic doesn't cure infertility, it does reduce stress and interference in the body and, more specifically, the nervous system. Reduction of aches and pains, together with improved blood and nerve flow, help set the stage for a healthy and functional pregnancy, birth and postpartum. Chiropractic can be a good complement to medical fertility treatments as well, mitigating some of the negative side effects of those treatments and helping to maximise their benefits.

CHINESE MEDICINE

Chinese medicine includes acupuncture, which is thought to reduce stress hormones and release endorphins, producing a profound state of relaxation. Regular acupuncture may result in hormonal regulation and balance, and needling specific acupoints aims to increase blood flow to the ovaries and uterus to stimulate ovulation and promote a healthy uterine lining.

Chinese herbal therapy works to nourish and strengthen the body by improving nutritional absorption, reducing inflammation, and regulating and balancing hormone levels. Practitioners custom blend herbs based on your particular needs. For men, acupuncture and herbs are commonly used to help the body increase and improve the quality, motility and quantity of sperm.

MASSAGE THERAPY

Two of the greatest benefits of massage are decreased stress and increased blood flow, both of which may help set the tone for a more fertile state. There are forms of 'fertility massage' that focus on the abdomen to reduce stress and increase blood flow directly to the womb, oviducts and ovaries and to improve 'alignment' of these organs.

Other modalities to consider include reflexology, meditation, hypnosis, yoga, nutritional therapy, homeopathic remedies and psychotherapy.

- Make sure you incorporate movement to increase blood flow. Get a massage once in a while. Do yoga or go for daily walks, and make this part of your routine.
- Eat healthily. Choose foods that are packed with nutrients that will help your body support a growing baby.
- Try to cut down on the stress in your life. If your job or personal life is stressful, do something to make a change. Try meditation or relaxing baths with essential oils like lavender and eucalyptus. Reducing stress encourages optimal fertility.
- Don't overthink it. As clichéd as it sounds – and immensely frustrating when in the throes of trying to conceive – calming the committee of your mind can only bring benefits. Letting go and allowing the process to unfold organically helps us to remember to stay present and shift our focus back to all the things we're currently grateful for in life.

WHAT CAN MY (MALE) PARTNER DO?

It's a common assumption that if there are problems with conception, there's an issue with the woman's reproductive system. However, according to Genea Australian Fertility Specialists, in about 40 per cent of cases where couples have trouble conceiving, the difficulty relates to the man and the quality or quantity of his sperm.[2] They offer the following tips for maintaining healthy sperm:

- Maintain a healthy weight – excess weight can affect sperm quality.
- Don't smoke or take recreational drugs, as both can affect sperm health and sex drive. Smoking in males also increases their partner's risk of miscarriage.
- Limit your alcohol consumption to no more than eight standard drinks per week.

- Some prescription medications can affect sperm health – see your doctor if you have concerns.
- Eat a healthy, balanced diet to facilitate healthy sperm production.
- Avoid spas, saunas, hot baths and putting a laptop on your lap, as warm temperatures can affect sperm production.

WHERE TO TURN IF YOU'RE NOT FALLING PREGNANT

Getting pregnant isn't always as simple as having sex during the fertile period and doing a handstand to help gravity do its thing! The good news is, there are many wonderful medical advances available these days to help you along if you're having trouble falling pregnant and staying pregnant.

Factors that can affect fertility:

- Endometriosis
- PCOS
- Damage to fallopian tubes or uterus
- Cervical issues
- Abnormality in the uterine shape
- Irregular cycles
- Age factor
- Male factor
- Obesity
- Substance abuse
- High levels of stress

If you've been trying for more than a year and you're under the age of 35, schedule an appointment with your doctor. If you're over the age of 35 (that's you elderly ladies out there reading with your spectacles on!) call your doctor if you've been trying for six months with no luck. There are tonnes of things the doctor can suggest outside of interventions, but if it comes down to it, here are a few ways science can help.

HCG 'FLUSHING'

This is a procedure that involves shooting an oil-soluble contrast media (a dye) up into your fallopian tubes to check for blockages. It can be uncomfortable, similar to some tough period cramps, but many women swear that this procedure alone helped get them pregnant the very next cycle. Although it's not conclusive, research has indicated that this kind of tubal flushing may improve the chance of pregnancy and live birth.

> **Teresa:** While I think getting pregnant with Forest was also a combined effort of letting go and embracing being present with Bodhi, I do not think it is a coincidence that the very next week after having a HCG done, we conceived our rainbow baby. I have two other friends who conceived the very next cycle after their procedure, too, and they swear that was what did it.

CLOMIFENE

This is a really useful medication that women experiencing ovulatory dysfunction can take to induce ovulation. The word on the street is that clomifene is one of the reasons we're seeing an increase in twin births, because multiple follicles are stimulated. It works wonders for many women, but it's not appropriate for all women experiencing fertility challenges. Check with your care provider about this option – it's typically the first step they'll suggest if getting pregnant is proving to be difficult.

Teresa: I took Clomid (a brand of clomifene) for one cycle a couple of months before I got pregnant with Forest. I wasn't ovulating regularly because I was still breastfeeding Bodhi. Clomid didn't work for me as it hyper stimulated my follicles. One grew to 40 mm before turning into a cyst that went away the next cycle. It just didn't work for my body, so I went off it the next cycle and focused on letting go of my obsession with getting pregnant (it had been twelve months of trying for number two at this point). Two months later I was pregnant with my rainbow baby.

TRIGGER SHOT

A trigger shot is an injection that is administered to a patient in order to force the body to ovulate. It can be used in conjunction with ovulation-stimulating drugs or utilising a patient's natural ovulation. Typically, the egg will be released 48 hours after the injection is given. It is either taken in the stomach or as an intramuscular shot.

Gemma Pranita: After twenty months of trying to conceive naturally and three months on a waitlist for IVF, I decided to give the trigger shot a go. I was put on a course of follicle stimulation hormone for two weeks. What gave me hope was that the procedure offered what felt like an exact science, the manufacturing of divine timing. Once it was established that an egg was ripe, I administered the trigger shot to force ovulation. We were incredibly lucky that it worked the first time. As someone who fell into the 'unidentified infertility' category, this trigger shot was the missing ingredient to help us conceive our sweet baby girl. While I know trigger shots don't work for everyone, it's a much less invasive route than IVF and we felt it was definitely worth pursuing as a first step.

An IUI often works in conjunction with the trigger shot and other ovulation medication (such as clomifine) but it can also be performed with a natural cycle. It involves your partner or donor giving a sperm sample, which is then placed into your uterine cavity using a catheter tube. Typically, medication is used to stimulate the growth of follicles/eggs and a trigger shot is used for timing accuracy. Some people experience some mild cramping or discomfort and they have you remain in a lying down position for 20 minutes after the procedure.

> **Teresa:** I have also tried this method of getting pregnant! It was twelve months into our journey trying to conceive baby number two and it was the month before I tried Clomid. We were monitored by my OB-GYN to see when ovulation was likely, then I drove to my doctor's house at 10 p.m. (trigger shot is suuuper specific, timing-wise!) to be administered the shot (right in the muscle of the buttocks, a bit ouchy!). I then flew to Arizona the next day, drove to grab sperm from my husband, who was at a fancy meditation retreat (aka rehab – and who convinced the staff that jerking off was a medical must and good for his recovery). I drove 90 minutes from there with said sperm in between my boozies to keep the little guys alive, arrived at the clinic, lay on the bed, had the spermies shot up there (didn't hurt a bit), then waited two weeks to test. All that and it was negative. Ah well, makes for a good story!

In-vitro fertilisation is a common procedure used by couples with fertility issues. IVF involves a doctor performing an egg retrieval on the woman and using the partner's or donor's sperm to fertilise the egg in a laboratory setting. The woman is administered stimulating drugs to help grow the follicles so that many mature eggs can be taken in the retrieval process, giving couples a higher chance of conceiving.

If fertilisation of the eggs is successful, the embryos will continue growing under very close supervision before being transferred (usually only one is transferred, but sometimes two) into the woman's uterus. There is also a growing trend to practise what's called 'natural IVF', which involves a minimal or zero stimulation cycle for those struggling with infertility. It's for those who are on a budget and/or fear how the high hormones in the stimulating drugs may affect their body. It's worth discussing natural IVF with your doctors, in case it's a good option for you.

IVF WITH PGD TESTING

This kind of IVF with additional embryo testing is offered in Australia in situations such as people who are predisposed to genetic disorders or who have experienced recurrent miscarriage. The embryos are tested to determine their health, and only healthy embryos will be transferred into mama.

INFERTILITY SUPPORT

If you're experiencing infertility, we highly recommend getting some emotional support, as it can be truly overwhelming, confusing and heartbreaking. Find people you can talk to, perhaps others who are in the trenches with you, or friends who have been there and have moved through it. Either way, you need to share what you're going through instead of bottling it inside. Here are some great websites offering support, knowledge and community. You are not alone.

www.varta.org.au

www.fertilitysupport.org.au

www.twoweekwait.com

Teresa: I experienced secondary infertility, which is infertility after already having one child. While my experience is nothing compared to those who have suffered years of struggles and losses, it still penetrated my heart in a way that is indescribable. I lived my life in two-week increments for fourteen months: two weeks until my fertile period when I could try to conceive, then two weeks to wait until I could test (a negative test or 'BFN', in forum speak), the same cycle over and over. It was ALL I could think about, day in, day out. Anyone pregnant around me triggered a deep sadness, as I just put on a brave face to be out in the world and showing up for my son. I obsessed over the age gap between Bodhi and the child who wasn't coming and spent many nights in tears. Finally I decided to get some help with my feelings by joining an online community that brought me strength and the support of folk who shared similar emotions and experiences. I started listening to some words by philosopher Alan Watts to calm my mind and find my Zen. I broke up with the idea of needing another child and started to pull myself back to a place of presence. I threw my everything into Bodhi and sure enough, after letting go of the fixation, I was pregnant with my sweet boy Forest. So while I know the 'just chill out' advice absolutely SUCKS, in my case I believe it really did make a huge difference.

ZEN NOTES

- Connect and communicate with your partner to ensure you're both on the same page. Stay open-minded and get intimate.
- Take a look at your current lifestyle and finances to see if you need to make any changes to help support a new family member.
- Find a healthcare practitioner you feel comfortable with and let them know about your plans to conceive. Ask them lots of questions; they can help you along the way.
- Clean up your act: eat nourishing foods, add in some supplements and move your body regularly.
- Get to know your body: track your ovulation pattern (and your cervical mucus!). This will help identify when you're most fertile.
- De-stress: create a stress-free (or low-stress) environment for yourself and find ways to relax. Add in a yoga class, read a book, have a bath or listen to a podcast.
- Seek further help and support if you need it. You're not alone on this journey, so reach out to a family member, a friend, a doctor or your partner.

PREGNANCY LOSS

TWO

I've noticed that most pregnancy books skip right over the topic of pregnancy loss, or mention it only briefly then move on – presumably to avoid putting readers off. However, Sarah and I decided that a chapter on pregnancy loss was integral to include, not only because it is so common, but also because it is a profoundly affecting part of many people's motherhood journey. If I'd known what to expect when I experienced the loss of my pregnancies, I don't think I would have felt so alone and ashamed. So, it's our hope that including this information can provide some insight and perhaps even a little comfort. It may be hard to read, and it was certainly painful to write, but it is important. We want to see more women sharing their stories, opening their hearts and sometimes exposing their wounds in order to comfort each other, creating a community of women willing to be brave, vulnerable and supportive of ourselves and our sisters. The more we talk about pregnancy loss, the less taboo and secretive it becomes.

Sarah: You will notice this chapter is written in Teresa's voice because when we first completed it, she was the only one of us who had experienced the grief of pregnancy loss. I have many friends who have experienced loss throughout different stages of pregnancy. My grandmother also suffered many losses in her years trying to have children. She didn't talk about it, but my mother said it was really hard on her. Teresa and I want to help alleviate the stigma surrounding pregnancy loss, and highlight that it's actually a very common experience – many more women than we probably realise have been through it. While it's important to be delicate with friends or family members who are going through it, the most helpful thing you can do is to take cues from them and check in on them, even if it's just to sit in silence – you don't always have to know the 'right thing' to say. This is a loss and they will be experiencing both physical and emotional pain. Be sensitive, but don't shy away because you don't understand it or aren't sure what to do. There's no right or wrong, and each individual will have different needs during this time. Be a safe place for your friend, as this is still a topic with so much stigma around it and so much that is unknown. They may feel isolated, confused and alone, all while trying to navigate the physical and emotional parts of their journey.

You'll notice I try to avoid the word 'miscarriage', because in my view it implies that women have 'mis' (meaning mistakenly) 'carried' their baby and that's why it has died. This continues to feed the flawed perception that women are to blame for the loss of our pregnancies. The overwhelming majority of pregnancy losses are caused by factors that are completely out of the mother's control. In fact, in first trimester pregnancy losses, typically it's the mother's healthy body recognising that the baby she is carrying is incompatible with life.[1] So let's throw this terminology out for the sake of this book (and maybe we can start a movement to get the word changed altogether!). Let's call it pregnancy loss, because that's what we are really talking about: the loss of our babies, not something we have done poorly.

MY STORY:
PREGNANCY LOSS

As I walked joyfully to the heartbeat scan appointment for our second baby, I was blissfully unaware of how my day was about to unfold. It had taken us six months to get pregnant the second time around, using acupuncture and ovulation sticks to try to enhance and pinpoint my fertile period. Finally the day had come that I'd envisioned since Bodhi was a baby: getting to see his sibling on the ultrasound screen! We waited excitedly to see our doctor, but after a couple of minutes of very quietly studying the ultrasound on the screen, her face fell. I won't ever forget that look. In that moment I knew our lives were about to be shattered. 'I'm so sorry, Teresa and Mark,' she said. 'This isn't a viable pregnancy.' The words sounded like they were being spoken in slow motion as the room spun. I clung to my toddler and wept into him, loud sobs I couldn't contain. My husband and I were stunned, unable to understand how or why this had happened.

The next few days were a blur of doctors and specialists before being ushered into a hospital bed and prepped for a dilation and curettage (D&C) to clear the lining of my uterus. This was the very first time I'd ever been in hospital or even had an operation. It was terrifying. After some pretty way-off guesses by doctors (including the possibility of conjoined twins) it was determined that I had suffered a molar pregnancy (see page 44). These are very rare, and can lead to all sorts of unpleasant health issues. I was made to feel like a medical anomaly.

The first week afterwards was the hardest because I was in emotional despair but had to be in mummy mode for Bodhi. About a week later I had to go overseas to shoot a movie, so I didn't have proper time to deal with my grief. Instead I just chose to ignore it, stuffing it as far down as possible. I channelled my pain into my work, which served the complex character I was portraying but ultimately didn't serve the actor behind her. I didn't allow myself to move through my feelings and, looking back now, I really wish I had done so, as they reared their heads in many different ways over the next few months. It was a very challenging period for my marriage.

Eventually what helped me was coming to terms with the notion that what I was most upset about was the thought of who this baby was going to be, the fabricated child I had made up in my mind: how he or she looked, smelt, what they were interested in and how they would bond with their big brother. Once I could recognise that baby was a fictional character my mind had created, I felt a little more settled in the reality of what had occurred, and accepted that this baby wasn't meant to be with us. I broke up with the idea of who they would've been and this gave me the healing I needed. I honoured the experience, made peace with it and decided to find hope again in the prospect of trying for another baby.

HOW LIKELY IS IT THAT I WILL SUFFER PREGNANCY LOSS?

There are tonnes of different studies with conflicting analysis out there, and the statistics are always being reworked and updated. So, I don't believe there is an evidence-based final answer for this, but what we can give you is an idea of the likelihood of experiencing pregnancy loss. The loss of pregnancy is much more common than we are led to believe – currently the estimate is that one in four women will experience it – but in fact many of these losses occur before we even realise we are pregnant.[2]

In the first trimester the risk of pregnancy loss falls with each passing week, with significant drops around the seven-week mark, and again after the twelve-week mark. Once the fetal heartbeat is detected, typically anywhere between six to eight weeks, you can breathe a bit easier, as pregnancy loss rates drop dramatically at this stage. (I've asked for an early seven-week scan for all of my pregnancies.) The age of the mother and the age of the biological father or donor, the number of prior losses and maternal health issues (discussed further below) can all affect the overall risk of losing a pregnancy.

COMMUNITY QUESTION: WHY DOES PREGNANCY LOSS OCCUR?

According to the Royal Women's Hospital, Victoria, approximately half of all pregnancy losses are due to abnormal chromosomes in the embryo, which prevent the pregnancy from developing as it should. For these abnormal embryos, miscarriage occurs as the body's natural response.[3] Some of my friends who have lost babies tell me they found this reason to be more comforting than others, as it showed them that their body was working properly, and they therefore knew that their baby wasn't compatible with life.

↘ Hormone imbalances

↘ Medical issues, in particular poorly controlled diabetes and thyroid disease

↘ Uterine or cervical abnormalities

↘ Lifestyle factors such as smoking, heavy drinking, recreational drug use and heavy caffeine intake

↘ Increased maternal and paternal age (the risk rises after about age 37 for women, and age 40 for men).[4]

PREVENTING PREGNANCY LOSS

Despite all our best efforts, whether we experience pregnancy loss or not is out of our hands. 'In most cases, there's nothing you can do to cause a miscarriage, and nothing you can do to prevent it,' says Siobhan Dolan, MD, a medical advisor to the mama and bub healthcare charity March of Dimes and an attending physician in the Division of Reproductive Genetics at Montefiore Medical Center in New York City.[5] While there is certainly no cheat sheet available to help you skip the experience of pregnancy loss, there are plenty of things you can do to ensure you're creating the optimal environment for your growing babe. Consult your doctor about minimising any risk factors created by your lifestyle. Understanding and accepting that, in most cases, pregnancy loss is unavoidable helps us to relinquish control and find a new way of moving through the experience.

PREGNANCY LOSS SIGNS AND SYMPTOMS

The sudden end of your pregnancy can only be confirmed by your healthcare provider, so these symptoms should not be used as a diagnosis. The symptoms of pregnancy loss are varying, but here are some of the more common ones to look out for:

- Vaginal bleeding, ranging from light spotting to heavy bleeding

- Passing blood clots, fluid or tissue from the vagina

- Abdominal pain or cramping

- Moderate to severe lower back pain

- Fever and chills

- Sudden decrease in pregnancy symptoms

- A later, longer and heavier than usual period (this is called a chemical pregnancy – more on that below).

If you suspect you're losing your pregnancy, contact your healthcare provider straight away so they can perform an ultrasound, or head directly to your emergency department to determine what is going on.

TYPES OF PREGNANCY LOSS

There are many different types of pregnancy loss. Your doctor or healthcare professional will be able to discuss these further with you. (You'll see below in the types of pregnancy losses listed that the term 'miscarriage' is often used – this is to align with medical terminology, even though we prefer to avoid the term generally.)

CHEMICAL PREGNANCY

A chemical pregnancy is a very early loss that occurs shortly after implantation – generally within five weeks – and can often be disguised as a late period that's heavier than usual. There may be light cramping, too. Many women who suffer from a chemical pregnancy won't even be aware they were pregnant in the first place, nor experience the typical early pregnancy signs. The cause of chemical pregnancy is still not totally clear, but some contributing factors may include issues with hormone levels, uterine abnormalities, advanced maternal age, chromosomal abnormalities and underlying maternal health issues such as thyroid disorders and blood clotting. Recovery and future conception are generally unproblematic – in my case, I experienced a chemical pregnancy in January 2018 and went on to conceive my daughter five months later.

THREATENED MISCARRIAGE

A threatened miscarriage doesn't necessarily mean you will lose your pregnancy. In fact, early bleeding and light cramping during pregnancy occurs in approximately a quarter of women, and half of these pregnancies will continue on healthily. Symptoms include light vaginal bleeding and mild abdominal cramping.

INEVITABLE MISCARRIAGE

An inevitable miscarriage is a pregnancy loss that is either expected to happen or comes without warning. Upon examination by a doctor it may become clear that the cervix has started to dilate, meaning pregnancy loss is impending. As well as a dilated cervix, symptoms include vaginal bleeding, uterine pain, cramping and tissue in the uterus.

COMPLETE MISCARRIAGE

This is a pregnancy loss during the first trimester in which the body completely clears the pregnancy tissue from the uterus. There may be heavy bleeding as well as moderate to severe abdominal cramping over a number of days. Passing of clots and tissue is also common, and an ultrasound done by your doctor can ensure that no tissue remains.

INCOMPLETE MISCARRIAGE

Unlike a complete miscarriage, sometimes the tissue from the baby does not entirely pass on its own. Symptoms of incomplete miscarriage include heavy bleeding, uncomfortable abdominal cramps, the passing of blood clots, lower back pain and nausea as the body tries to empty itself. If there's any sign of infection or too much discomfort, medication may be required, or the lost pregnancy may be removed surgically through a D&C.

MISSED MISCARRIAGE

This kind of pregnancy loss can feel especially hard because it often lacks symptoms. The fetus stops growing at some point during the pregnancy, but your body doesn't expel the pregnancy and may in fact continue to give you signals that all is well with your baby – this is also referred to as a silent miscarriage. You may only find out that the pregnancy has ended at an ultrasound. In some cases, women may experience the more typical symptoms of pregnancy loss, such as light bleeding and cramping.

If you've suffered a missed miscarriage, it could mean that the fetus's genetic material wasn't compatible with life. Luckily, the majority of women who suffer this kind of pregnancy loss go on to have a healthy and uneventful pregnancy.

RECURRENT MISCARRIAGE

This is a term used for women who have had multiple losses, typically three or more in succession. While there is no one main cause of recurrent miscarriage, it is thought that some factors may have an influence, such as obesity, smoking, hormonal imbalances, genetic issues and increased maternal age.[6]

If you have a history of pregnancy loss, discuss this with your doctor – they may be able to investigate the causes and refer you to a specialist. The good news is that many women who have experienced more than one miscarriage do go on to have an uneventful future pregnancy.

ECTOPIC PREGNANCY

This type of loss occurs in about 2 per cent of pregnancies, when the egg implants itself in a location outside of the uterus, most commonly the fallopian tubes. An ectopic pregnancy can also develop outside the fallopian tubes (e.g. in the ovary, cervix or somewhere in the abdominal cavity), but this is even less common. An ectopic pregnancy is sadly not viable and, if left untreated, can pose serious health risks for the mother. Symptoms include severe abdominal pain (usually isolated to one side), pain in the tip of one shoulder, diarrhoea and vomiting, lightheadedness, vaginal bleeding or spotting and bowel pain. Urgent medical attention should be sought if these symptoms occur. Subsequent pregnancies will need to be closely monitored in the early stages, as the risk of a second ectopic pregnancy is higher than for those who have never experienced one.

COMPLETE MOLAR PREGNANCY

This occurs when an egg that doesn't contain any genetic information is fertilised by one or two sperm. A fetus never develops, and the cells that typically create the placenta instead form hundreds of abnormal cells into a tumour called a hydatidiform mole. It is a type of gestational trophoblastic disease and is signalled by abnormally high HCG levels (which may cause increased pregnancy symptoms), an enlarged uterine area and painless bleeding at around 4–5 months' gestation. Treatment is almost always surgical in nature.

PARTIAL MOLAR PREGNANCY

This is similar to a complete molar pregnancy except there is the beginning of a fetus growing alongside the hydatidiform mole. There may also be normal placental tissue growing alongside the abnormal placental tissue. Like a complete molar pregnancy, a partial one is a genetic accident – in almost all cases, the fetus is chromosomally abnormal and sadly cannot survive. Symptoms include high blood pressure, increased pregnancy symptoms, an enlarged uterine area and vaginal bleeding. Again, surgery is often required to remove the molar pregnancy.

Like a complete molar pregnancy, a blighted ovum never contains a fetus – the placenta and pregnancy sac grow but an embryo never develops due to unknown factors that prevent the embryo cells from multiplying. Sometimes it is detected at a routine ultrasound appointment, and it can be shocking to discover that the earlier positive pregnancy test result was actually caused by rising HCG levels from the developing placenta, rather than a fertilised egg. Minor abdominal cramps and vaginal bleeding may occur as the body starts to shed blood and tissue from the uterus.

STILLBIRTH

An early stillbirth is a fetal death occurring between weeks 20 and 27 of pregnancy, and a late stillbirth occurs between weeks 28 and 36 of pregnancy. A term stillbirth occurs after week 37 of pregnancy. In Australia an average of six babies are stillborn per day.[7] In about 20 per cent of the cases the cause of death remains unknown.[8] In the remaining cases it has been found that stillbirth is caused by congenital abnormalities of the baby, placenta malfunction including placental abruption, an infection or high blood pressure in the mother, complications during labour, pre-eclampsia, and issues such as umbilical cord trauma.[9] If a baby dies in utero, they will need to be birthed through a vaginal or caesarean delivery. Some women choose to allow their body to go into labour naturally, which can take up to two weeks, while many families decide induction is the preferred option for delivery. After delivery there is the opportunity for the parents to hold the baby in their arms.

Symptoms and warning signs can include strong abdominal or back pain, fever or chills, dizziness and blurred vision, nausea and vomiting and painful swelling, including of the hands and feet. There may be a change in the movement pattern of the baby, including a sudden increase in activity or reduced movement, and bright red vaginal bleeding or a sudden increase in vaginal discharge.

A stillbirth is deeply traumatic and distressing for loved ones, and delivery can be a very emotionally challenging experience. There are excellent organisations in Australia, such as SANDS Australia, that provide support to those who have experienced stillbirth. (See page 53 for contact details.)

According to the Stillbirth Foundation, it is not known whether stillbirth can be prevented, but there are ways in which we can try to ensure the best possible outcome for baby. These practices include monitoring movement through kick counts and movement diaries during the third trimester, taking folic acid prior to and throughout pregnancy, getting scans to rule out growth restriction and other risks, eating a healthy, well-supplemented diet and coming up with a management plan with your doctor to treat health issues such as hypertension and diabetes.[10]

AFTER PREGNANCY LOSS

DEALING WITH GRIEF

Everyone deals with grief differently, and there's no 'right' or 'wrong' way to feel after the loss of a pregnancy. During this challenging period it's very common for women to isolate themselves and switch off from the outside world, and while a little of this can be deeply healing, it's also important to understand the value of communication with those who love us the most. Accepting comfort from our partner, friends and family is a beautiful way to help develop a sense of trust and hope in the world again. Let your loved ones hold you up and help you through this time – and remember that they will be grieving in their own ways too. Seek additional support from a doctor or trained counsellor if you're experiencing helplessness and depression that feel relentless and overwhelming and don't diminish over time.

It's also worth bearing in mind the large hormonal shifts (as well as the physical ones) that can occur when a pregnancy is lost, as the body readjusts from being pregnant. This can be a factor in how we respond to the loss. It takes time for physical and emotional wounds to heal, so allow yourself plenty of time to recover.

Memories are important, and doing something ritualistic and ceremonial can be a beautiful way of remembering our lost little ones. If you've lost a baby through stillbirth, you may want to keep mementos such as the hospital bracelet, photos, locks of hair and your baby's handprints and footprints. These items can become very treasured items, and may be helpful to you in the grieving process. Rituals could involve saying a prayer or planting a flower in your garden – a spot for your baby's life to be thought of and celebrated. Some women release balloons, others get together with friends and have a blessing ceremony. You'll feel it out and determine what is the right choice for you.

Some parents really love to be able to talk about their babies and be open with their experiences. Sometimes friends and well-meaning family members think it's taboo to discuss the loss of a pregnancy, or that you won't want to talk about it, but if you do want to talk about it openly, you can gently let your support network know that this is part of the healing process for you.

Personally, I really appreciated hearing others share their stories. It made me feel less alone, and there was something really empowering about women sitting around together sharing stories of grief and disappointment and creating an accepting and loving space for our babies to exist in our words and stories. It felt sacred to me, and it was a way of honouring our little ones. Being able to swing between being the guided and supported and being the giver and supporter was a beautiful give-and-take experience that felt both deeply moving and healing.

TRYING TO CONCEIVE AGAIN AFTER LOSS

Every mother will have a different experience regarding conceiving again after losing their angel baby (the baby lost in utero). Some women really don't feel ready to conceive again until well after a year or more has passed, others choose not to try to conceive again at all – each emotional and physical journey is unique. You and your partner are the best judges of when it feels right to try again. Chat to your doctor, ensure you're in a healthy place with your grief, give your body enough time to recover and then make lots of sweet love with your partner.

The good news is that if you have had one miscarriage, the next pregnancy will most likely be normal.[11] This can bring both reassurance and hope.

Personally, I wanted to immediately get pregnant again after our loss – in fact, I had Mark change travel plans so we could try to conceive the very next cycle after my D&C. I was a mess, and just figured that getting pregnant again would wash all the pain away. It would be seven months before we conceived again and it felt like an eternity – I kid you not when I say I almost lost the plot at month six! In retrospect, I can now say that I'm so grateful it took that long. It afforded me time to get into a better and more balanced headspace; my body needed to heal and so did my heart. I needed to come back to a place of equilibrium from where I could enter my rainbow pregnancy (a pregnancy following a miscarriage) with a clear mind and a hopeful spirit.

My good friend Tahyna MacManus (nee Tozzi) conceived on the very next cycle after her first loss and she went on to have a beautiful healthy baby girl. (She also went on to direct a documentary about pregnancy loss that I was privileged to take part in called *M.O.M Misunderstandings of Miscarriage*, a must-watch that aims to shatter the shame and stigma around pregnancy loss.) Tahyna's rainbow baby, Echo, came straight after the loss of her first baby and she found Echo's pregnancy very healing. A recent study published in the journal *Obstetrics & Gynecology* suggests that perhaps there's benefit in conceiving so soon after a loss – the study found that women who try to conceive within three months of a loss may have a greater likelihood of falling pregnant again and having a live birth.[12] Food for thought.

MY STORY:
PREGNANCY AFTER LOSS

Fortunately, the next time I conceived after my loss it was a successful and healthy journey, and resulted in the birth of my son Forest. It had been a total of fourteen months since we first started trying for our second baby when we welcomed him into the world. I know many couples endure a much longer wait than that, but for us at the time it felt never-ending.

Looking back on my pregnancy with Forest now, I realise just how much anxiety I experienced in those first few months. I'd convinced myself I had secondary infertility and took myself off to a fertility specialist. They determined that I wasn't ovulating regularly because I was still breastfeeding Bodhi, who was almost two. I took the specialist's advice to leave eight hours between breastfeeds and, amazingly, the next month I was pregnant.

I was terrified though – I knew I had a slightly higher chance of having a subsequent molar pregnancy than women who hadn't experienced one before. I assumed it wouldn't end well again. I was keen to have regular monitoring, so we booked in weekly scans for the first twelve weeks to ease my mind.

My bestie, Cass, came with me to my first scan at five weeks. I anticipated bad news and was so grateful that Cass was hugging me and holding my hand as we walked in there. The technician noticed my tears and asked if I'd had a bad experience before. I just nodded and tried to compose myself as I waited for the bad news – but it didn't come. Everything was progressing fine. I cried again – this time with relief – and immediately called Mark, who cried back from the other end of the phone.

As each week and each scan passed without drama, I gradually started to return to that place of trust and comfort in my pregnancy that I'd had when carrying my Bodhi. I realised now that I'd breezed through my first pregnancy blissfully unaware of all the complications and heartbreak so many women experience on their journey to having a baby. Every now and then throughout my rainbow babe's pregnancy, the rush of anxiety would hit me – fear would start to creep in and morbid thoughts would begin to swirl. But we made it through, and when I was lucky enough to have my son in my arms, it was with a renewed appreciation that the miracle of childbirth has no guarantees.

What I realise now is that women who go on to get pregnant after loss need support, gentle understanding and a loving community of people to pick them up when their worry becomes overwhelming. It's imperative that these women don't get overlooked. Often they suffer in silence, endure isolation in their fear and feel guilty for not experiencing the elation that everyone else expects of them with this new and healthy pregnancy. Love and compassion go a very long way. Pregnancy and conception aren't always straightforward and uncomplicated – we shouldn't assume anything is easy. Let's band together to encourage, uplift and embrace each other throughout this journey, all the peaks and valleys of it.

SARAH'S STORY

My original contribution to this chapter was about how to be a good friend to someone who has experienced a loss. But as we reached the final edit of this book, my situation changed. I was newly pregnant with my third child, and after seeing our babe's little heartbeat flickering away merrily at 6.5 weeks pregnant, I believed all was smooth sailing.

At our 8-week appointment the ultrasound technician had barely touched the wand to my tummy when she quickly took it off and said she needed to use the wand that went inside of me to get a better look. She told me it was because my bladder was full, but I knew something had shifted when the nurse left the room to go and fetch our doctor. My heart sank. I turned to my husband, who was sitting next to our six-year-old, and I said, 'This isn't good news.' He held my hand and when our doctor came back in the room, he asked me a few questions before telling me our sweet baby's heartbeat was gone. I just stared at the screen, half-listening to what he was saying next. He said, 'The first thing you need to know is this isn't your fault.' I thought *yes, I know that*. My ears were ringing and I just kept staring at him trying to process what was happening inside of me. I heard a little noise to my left and I saw my son, and we began to explain what was happening. My doctor spoke beautifully to him as tears started flowing down my cheeks. I know the statistics, I have read the stories and I knew this was possible, but you cannot predict how you will feel in the moment. I was genuinely shocked when it happened.

While it is so painful to add my voice in this new way, re-reading this chapter has offered me great comfort. I lay curled in a ball, reading over the pages as the tears flooded my face. I wanted to see the stories with new eyes. It has reminded me that I don't walk this path alone and reaffirms why this chapter in our book is so important.

PREGNANCY HELP AUSTRALIA

Assisting women and families who may be experiencing difficulties as
a result of a pregnancy or suffering a pregnancy loss.

www.pregnancysupport.com.au

1300 792 798 (QLD, NSW, VIC or ACT) / 1300 655 156 (SA, WA, TAS or NT)

PREGNANCY, BIRTH AND BABY

Call for trusted advice and emotional support from registered child nurses
between 7 a.m. and midnight, seven days a week.

www.pregnancybirthbaby.org.au

1800 882 436

SANDS

Sands provides support, information and education to anyone affected
by the death of a baby before, during or shortly after birth. Many of the
volunteers offering support over the telephone are parents who have also
suffered loss. Support is available 24 hours a day, seven days a week.

www.sands.org.au

1300 072 637

BEARS OF HOPE

Provides grief support and care for families who experience the loss
of their baby.

www.bearsofhope.org.au

1300 11 HOPE

ZEN NOTES

- ⌁ Pregnancy loss occurs in an average of one in four pregnancies.
- ⌁ There are many different types of pregnancy loss, most of which are not preventable.
- ⌁ More often than not, pregnancy loss is our body's natural way of recognising that a baby's genetic makeup isn't compatible with life.
- ⌁ If you notice any of the signs or symptoms discussed in this chapter, contact your healthcare practitioner immediately.
- ⌁ Everyone deals with pregnancy loss in their own way. Reach out to trusted members of your community to help you through. There are also support networks (listed above) that can be invaluable.

PREGNANCY

THREE

Congratulations, you're preggo! You're about to embark on ten months (40 weeks) of the most amazing, alarming, mind-boggling, challenging and life-changing experiences. This chapter will thrust you (no pun intended) into all the vomit, sweat, leaks and goop involved in pregnancy. We'll look at the fluctuations, emotions and hormones that carrying new life brings, as well as the exquisiteness and empowerment of this special process. Each pregnancy is different, so take what applies to you and ditch the rest! Welcome to this wild journey: you are *growing a human being*. It doesn't get wilder than that.

SHARING THE NEWS

WITH YOUR PARTNER

If you've been trying to conceive, it can be almost impossible to hold back from daydreaming about the moment you find out you are pregnant, and even harder not to imagine how you will share the news with your partner. There are so many ways to reveal you're expecting, so get creative and enjoy the experience.

Sarah: I had thought about what it would feel like to see a pregnancy test with two lines. I had an actual dream I was carrying a litter of golden retriever puppies. I had wondered how I would tell Eric, and then imagined our conversation in full (about the pregnancy, not the puppies!). On the day when I got those fateful two lines – one very dark, one faint – I went to a shop in town and bought a onesie, a little book and some baby booties. I then drove home, wrapped it all up in a box, taped the pregnancy test to the inside and waited for Eric to get home. When he did, I told him I had found a box of stuff I wanted him to go through. He didn't touch that box for a half hour until I mentioned it again, trying to get him to look inside. Finally persuaded, he stared inside for a moment or two then looked up at me and said, 'Wait a minute, are you pregnant?' I of course screamed 'YES!'

Teresa: Mark and I had been trying to get pregnant for about six months. When I found out I was finally pregnant I was in Edmonton, Canada shooting *Cut Bank*. I immediately ran out to get a bunch more tests that were all positive too. I was giddy with excitement and filmed myself, a crying and blubbering mess of emotions. I stashed the video to share with Mark later. That afternoon I started to plot the master reveal. I knew I'd be seeing Mark for Father's Day back in LA in a few days, so I took aaaall the positive pregnancy tests and stuck them on a black piece of cardboard and wrote *Pregnant!* above each one. On Father's Day, Isaac, my stepson, and I took Mark on a surprise Father's Day picnic where I gave him his special gift with a card written from the baby. I had wrapped a little crocheted brown baby top and hand-knitted booties in with the black cardboard with all the tests stuck to it. Cue the famous Mark Webber happy tears!

WITH FRIENDS, FAMILY AND EVERYONE ELSE

A question that comes up a lot in our mum groups is, *When is the right time to tell your friends and family?* This is a really personal question, and the answer is different for everyone.

We both chose to tell those closest to us much earlier than the recommended 'go public' advice of 13 weeks gestation. Why? Well, firstly, that's a pretty old-fashioned stance – pregnancy loss is common and these days much more openly discussed. The people we shared our happy news with are the same people we would turn to in the event of a pregnancy loss. Ask yourself this: if something unexpected were to happen and your pregnancy didn't continue, who would you be talking to? Perhaps these folks are the same people you'll call, giddy with glee, after your first heartbeat scan, or after you've peed on your 59th pregnancy test.

If waiting is more your style, there is no pressure to share the news before you are ready. Once a heartbeat has been detected and you enter your second trimester at week 13, the rate of miscarriage lessens significantly. According to one Australian study on 697 women, the overall risk of having a miscarriage after seeing a fetal heartbeat (7 weeks' gestation) was about 4 per cent, and at 8 weeks, with a normal prenatal visit and no vaginal bleeding, that drops to 1.6 per cent. This risk drops every week between 6 and 9 weeks.[1]

Many people choose to wait until this point. We both told our families and closest friends in our first trimester, and then publicly announced the news during our second trimester. Chat to your partner, make a list of the people in your life and figure out who you'll announce to and when. It's super fun coming up with ways to tell the world you've got a babe on board!

Sarah: When I fell pregnant with my first child and was 7 or 8 weeks along, I called Teresa and asked her to come over for coffee. I could hardly contain myself after our initial hugs and hellos, and basically belted out of my lungs: 'I'M PREGNANT!' We were both crying and laughing – it was such a special moment that I will never forget. I knew that no matter what happened I would be sharing every step of my journey with Teresa, so I wanted her to know from the beginning.

Teresa: With my first pregnancy, I told my besties and parents between 5 and 8 weeks by sending them a video of my OB-GYN pointing to Bodhi's little six-week-old fetal pole and saying 'Look at that happy happy little heartbeat!' With my second pregnancy, which ended in a loss, I told a much larger group of people at 5 weeks pregnant. I had to sheepishly retract my 'I'm pregnant!' statement over the coming weeks. At the time it was pretty hard as I had just blurted out my pregnancy news to anyone and everyone I bumped into. For the following months I'd see random people I'd forgotten I had told, and they were very confused when I didn't have a bump. It was awkward for anyone not in my inner circle, and emotional for me to have to explain what had happened. I found myself brushing it off and quickly changing the subject. With my subsequent pregnancies, I decided to wait until after their first heartbeat scans to yell it from the rooftops!

Some women wonder when they have to let their employer know they are pregnant. This can be a sensitive subject – some people worry they will be treated differently, or fear losing their jobs as a result, even though such action is against the law. You may have to give as much as ten weeks' notice for your leave, with written dates submitted four weeks prior, stating the beginning and end of your maternity leave. For more information about your rights and also the Australian Government Paid Parental Leave Scheme, see fairwork.gov.au. Check the laws in your state or territory and your employment contract for specifics regarding paid parental leave entitlements for you and your partner (this also applies for surrogacy and adoption).

GOOD NUTRITION FOR MAMA MEANS NUTRIENTS FOR BABY

Eating well has lifelong benefits for growth and development, and good nutrition during conception and pregnancy will be a vital factor in your child's long-term health. Before you panic about what you have (or haven't) eaten in recent weeks, take heart. As Australian naturopath and nutritionist Maria Harpas says: 'If you're already pregnant, stop worrying! You haven't failed the planning stage. Keep in mind that most mums don't know they have a baby on board till well past the first month, so if you missed the opportunity for preconception prep . . . you're in the majority!'

Throughout your pregnancy you may hear a lot about all the foods you can't eat – but what about the ones you should? Nutrient-dense foods are one of the best sources of the essential vitamins your baby will need to grow and develop during pregnancy. The common nutrients that are important for your growing baby are folate, omega-3s, calcium, vitamin D, iodine and iron.

VITAMINS AND MINERALS

FOLATE

As explained in Chapter 1, it's essential that you consume folate every day during your first three months of pregnancy, so continue the 400-microgram intake that you (hopefully) began one month pre-pregnancy.

CALCIUM AND VITAMIN D

Other important vitamins are calcium and vitamin D: these work together to help build your baby's bones and teeth. Milk, cheese, yoghurt and sardines are great sources of calcium, but if you have trouble digesting dairy or choose not to consume animal products, you can actually get an impressive amount of calcium from foods such as dark leafy greens, broccoli, and of course from a calcium supplement.

You can head outside, stand in the gorgeous sunshine and get a healthy dose of vitamin D that way! We sometimes forget that we get most of our vitamin D from the sun. Just be careful not to overdo it and get sunburnt. You can also obtain a small amount of vitamin D from foods such as eggs, oily fish, margarine, fortified milks and supplements – some of which come in a liquid form to drop into water.

OMEGA-3

DHA and EPA are two types of long-chain omega-3 fatty acids found in fish and algae. (There are also short-chain fatty acids, but they don't have the same benefits for pregnant women as long-chain fatty acids.) There are many benefits to eating food containing DHAs and EPAs while pregnant: they have been known to increase milk supply, support babies' visual and cognitive development and prevent preterm delivery.[2] The recommended intake to obtain the sufficient amount of omega-3 from fish is two to three 150-gram servings of low-mercury fish, such as salmon, herring, trout or anchovies, per week. If your diet does not include enough DHA and EPA and it is not included in your prenatal vitamin, consider taking a separate omega-3 supplement.

Don't eat fish? What many people don't realise is that fish get these essential fatty acids from the marine microalgae they eat in their natural environment. There are now animal-free sources of omega-3 available such as Green Nutritionals' GreenOMEGA3 supplement.

A woman's need for iron increases during pregnancy because her baby is drawing enough iron from her to last them months after they are born. Although meat is a great source of iron, you can also get your daily dose from other iron-rich foods such as green leafy vegetables, dried beans and lentils. Vitamin C actually improves iron absorption in the body, so for maximum benefits combine your iron-rich foods with foods containing vitamin C. Most prenatal vitamins contain iron, but you can also take separate iron supplements to boost your levels. Check with your doctor before taking iron supplements while pregnant, though, because overdosing on iron can be poisonous.

IODINE

Iodine is a nutrient found in salt water. You might sometimes see it in an ingredient list as an additive. According to the National Health and Medical Research Council:

Through mandatory fortification, most of the Australian population will get enough iodine, meaning women of child bearing age should enter pregnancy with adequate iodine intake. However, the extra iodine available through bread is not enough to meet the additional needs of pregnancy and during breastfeeding. The National Health and Medical Research Council recommends that all women who are pregnant, breastfeeding or considering pregnancy take an iodine supplement of 150 micrograms each day. Women with pre-existing thyroid conditions should seek advice from their medical practitioner prior to taking a supplement.

Seaweed, seafood and other salt water plants contain iodine. You can also get the amount you need by taking a prenatal multivitamin.

For those who like to see the numbers,
here are the recommended daily intakes:

Folate: 400 micrograms

Iron: 27 milligrams (found in most prenatal vitamins)

Calcium: 1000 milligrams

Vitamin D: 400 international units

Omega-3 (DHA): 500 milligrams

Iodine: 150 micrograms

WHAT WE DIDN'T KNOW: TRYING DIFFERENT PRENATAL VITAMINS

There are a lot of options when it comes to prenatal vitamins. Sometimes it's possible to try before you buy, but if not, we suggest buying the smallest bottle you can, to start with, because some can make you nauseated – it's important to find the brand that works for you. Try taking them at night with food, but make sure you're also drinking plenty of water. Look for whole-food based vitamins, which may be easier on your stomach. Another great option is organic gummy prenatal vitamins: perfect if you don't like taking a pill!

FOODS TO AVOID DURING PREGNANCY

We hear a lot about what foods to eat or avoid during pregnancy – some take a militant approach to abiding by these lists while others keep the suggested no-nos as a loose guide. With your own research and direction from your care provider, you can choose what to eat and what to avoid during pregnancy, but here are some main things to consider steering clear of. (Ask your care provider for the most recent guide.)

- Raw meat: rare and undercooked beef or poultry should be avoided because of the risk of contamination with coliform bacteria, toxoplasmosis or salmonella.

- Deli meats, including poultry, hot dogs, fermented meats, sausages:

the risk here is listeria (see below). It's best to reheat these products, even if the package states that they are fully cooked, in order to avoid listeria – the suggested temperature is 74°C.

- Smoked seafood: listeria can be found in smoked, lox, nova style, kippered or fish jerky products.
- Raw seafood including shellfish: it's best to avoid anything raw during pregnancy.
- Fish high in mercury: all types of tuna (except canned), yellowtail, swordfish, tilefish, sea bass etc. (This can vary geographically).
- Raw eggs (and anything made with raw eggs), including some foods you may not immediately think of, such as cake batter and Caesar salad dressing.
- Seafood salad, chicken salad, egg salad: may contain listeria.
- Unpasteurised juice, milk or beverages including freshly squeezed juices.
- Soft cheeses made from unpasteurised milk, including brie, feta, camembert, roquefort, queso blanco and queso fresco. If you're unsure whether a cheese is raw, ask the server.
- Raw or undercooked sprouts: clover, mung bean, alfalfa, radish. These may contain E. coli or salmonella.
- Salads, unless freshly prepared.
- Foods you know you are intolerant to, as they will affect your immune system.
- Alcohol: the NHMRC says not drinking is the safest option. (Fetal alcohol spectrum disorders can cause physical and learning problems, developmental delays, impulsiveness, problems socialising, ADHD and behaviour control issues and may not be recognised until school age.)
- Caffeine: up to 200 milligrams per day can be consumed.

Listeria are bacteria that can cause serious issues such as infections and blood poisoning. These health issues can have devastating effects on a pregnant mother and her baby – complications can include miscarriage, stillbirth, premature birth or a baby who is very ill once born.[3] To avoid food containing dangerous bacteria, eat freshly cooked foods, wash fruit and vegetables before eating, do not reheat food that is more than a day old, and be careful to reheat foods thoroughly before consuming.

FOODS TO LIMIT DURING PREGNANCY

Just as in life pre-pregnancy, moderation is key! We don't want to rain on your parade and pregnancy cravings are real – Teresa had a real thing for chocolate croissants during hers. So, we're putting this list of foods in the 'you may want to limit' category rather than the 'it's safer to avoid' one.

- Junk food, foods that are high in sugar, processed foods with hidden additives such as hot chips, chocolate, biscuits, cakes, nuggets, lollies, soft drinks, ice creams, pastries, etc.
- Industrial trans-fats: usually found in junk food (as above), as well as margarine, mass-produced icing, microwave popcorn, flavoured drinks, fried foods.
- Don't eat the same foods day in, day out. Eat a variety of fresh, colourful food, which will vary the nutrients your body has access to, and try to eat seasonal produce where possible.
- The biggest fish in the ocean will contain the highest amounts of mercury. Exposure to mercury can damage a baby's growing brain and nervous system, so stick to smaller fish such as salmon, butterfish, shrimp, crab, trout etc.

If you have any questions at all, just ask your care provider. We know that all this nutritional information is a lot to process, but once you've taken it in, try not to stress. You'll find your way through.

THE FIRST TRIMESTER

Okay! Time to get into the trimesters. Each trimester will be unique, complex and not without its valleys – but don't worry, there will be plenty of peaks, too! We are gonna take you through the weeks of your pregnancy Zen Mama–style, and show you how we document and talk about all that comes with having a baby on board!

The first trimester can be a stressful time for a lot of women. Your body goes through so much in the first 13 weeks (gas, bloating, nausea, your pants no longer fitting . . .). Your hormones might go a bit bonkers, too. Time has now taken on a new meaning, and you may find yourself measuring it with things like fruit or animal sizes! You may experience a lot of firsts: ultrasounds, blood tests, hearing the heartbeat, learning the sex of the baby (depending on which tests and scans you have when). You may also encounter puke fests, head spins and nausea hitting you like a high-speed train – remember, this too shall pass!

If you're anything like us, you're probably counting the weeks, waiting patiently and anxiously for the second trimester to roll in so you can feel that much more secure and safe. A lot of questions arise during this time, and a lot of mamas tend to feel overwhelmed by all the new information they're trying to take in. Hopefully in this section we can help you feel a bit more at ease. We won't be able to offer ALL the definitive information on pregnancy in this chapter (there's so much!), but there are other books out there that are complete in-depth bibles, such as *Pregnancy, Childbirth, and the Newborn* by Penny Simkin, *Up the Duff* by Kaz Cooke and Dr. William Sears' *The Healthy Pregnancy Book*, which we loved. This chapter is based on our own experiences, the things we found challenging and what worked best for us along our journey.

Remember, you cannot control the next ten months; your body will be doing all the work for you. What you *can* control is your state of mind, how you approach each day and how you nourish your body and your soul. As every new thing unfolds and the weeks pass, try to allow yourself the gift of acceptance. Your body is already working so hard to grow this life inside you, the best thing you can do for yourself and your baby is to give your body a lot of love and self-care.

WEEKS 3—5

You may not even realise you are pregnant in these first few weeks! The reason we don't talk about weeks 1–3 during pregnancy is because technically you're not pregnant yet. It is difficult to know exactly when you conceive, so care providers calculate conception from the first day of your last menstrual cycle. When you do find out you are pregnant, your doctor will most likely ask you to come in to confirm your pregnancy. This is usually done by taking your blood and measuring your HCG level (the pregnancy hormone). For some high-risk patients they may ask you to come in for a follow-up HCG check to ensure the number is rising, and they'll often check the levels of your hormones such as progesterone and oestrogen, which help support a healthy pregnancy.

During this period of time you may only notice very subtle changes on the outside, but inside, your body is working in overdrive. For a start, the baby's umbilical cord and placenta are beginning to form, surrounded by a yolk sac! You may also have some super awesome early pregnancy signs like diarrhoea, gas, bloating, a sniffly nose and sore boobies.

JOURNALLING

Despite some of the less pleasant side effects, this might be a nice time to start journalling your experience. We love documenting our pregnancies – there's something so touching about going back and being reminded of your experience: the emotions, symptoms and stories. This can be particularly useful during subsequent pregnancies, and it can also be a lovely thing to share with your kids when they get older. If you want to track your pregnancy journey, you can follow the format we use on our blog by recording the answers to these questions every week or two:

- What week?
- How big is the baby?
- What's something new this week?
- Most challenging moment?
- Most exciting moment?
- Starting weight
- Current weight
- Movement
- Meals
- Food aversions
- Cravings
- Reflections

COMMUNITY QUESTION: SHOULD I BE CHANGING MY PERSONAL CARE AND CLEANING PRODUCTS?

This question comes up a lot – little hands will be touching all the floors, tables and walls in your home, so it's only natural to think about the effects of particular household chemicals. Indeed, a small meta-analysis of sixteen studies by Harvard public health researchers found an association between childhood exposure to indoor insecticides and a higher risk of certain childhood cancers. More research is needed to ensure we fully understand the health impacts of these chemicals in our homes.[4] You may choose to avoid cleaning with or handling toxic chemicals when growing a baby in your body – if you inhale or swallow some chemicals, it's possible for them to enter your bloodstream and be passed on to your baby via the placenta.[5] We know: until we were thinking of having babies this never occurred to us, either!

So, think of this as a moment to cleanse your home and your body of toxins, and consider switching to natural disinfectants, certified organic products and skincare. A midwife gave us this wonderful tip: if you can't pronounce an ingredient or don't recognise it, you probably shouldn't be using it! Going all-natural doesn't have to be expensive. Our friend and expert Aida Garcia-Toledo, founder of Non-Toxic Munchkin, gave us her favourite tips for homemade cleaning products and personal care.

What are we exposing our bodies and developing babies to every single day through personal care and cleaning products? A lot. In fact, most babies today are born with over 200 chemicals in their umbilical cord blood and, yes, many of these are chemicals commonly used in cosmetics, personal care and cleaning products.

Think of it this way: most of what we eat, use on our skin, and breathe in makes its way to our developing baby. While many chemicals in the products we use are found in very small concentrations, if you count every single ingredient in every single product we use in our home and our body every single day, small amounts can add up fast. This cumulative effect is what can, and often does, have an impact on the short- and/or long-term health of the developing baby (and its mama's health too).

Ironically, before cosmetic and cleaning companies convinced us all that we had to use the costliest product on the market with the newest technology and filled with exotic artificial smells and chemicals we can't pronounce, women were using products that came from nature that have amazing protective and effective properties – without the added chemicals.

PERSONAL CARE

Here are some easy tips to follow that will help you avoid harmful chemicals in personal care products.

    1. Look in your kitchen. Oils you might already have in your pantry are actually proven to be amazing moisturisers and can even help avoid stretch marks: pure almond oil, coconut oil, grapeseed oil and jojoba oil all can be used all over your body after you shower. If you dislike the oily finish, shea butter and cocoa butter work well too.

2. Use less. A good rule of thumb during pregnancy is to streamline your daily beauty routine. By using fewer products, you will automatically expose yourself, and your developing baby, to a reduced number of potentially harmful chemicals.

3. Make your own beauty products. It might sound like a lot of work but it can be super easy and the best thing is that you know exactly what ingredients are in the final product.

SOME OF MY FAVOURITE DIY BEAUTY RECIPES

BODY SCRUB

Store-bought body scrubs are often pricey and filled with artificial fragrance. Making your own body scrub is an incredibly easy and cost-effective alternative: just mix 1 cup of organic granulated brown sugar with ½ cup olive oil. Store in a small sealed mason jar.

BODY BUTTER

I was looking for a smoother texture than shea butter and found this super simple recipe which I have kept going back to over the years. Melt 1 cup shea butter and ½ cup coconut oil in the top of a double boiler. Remove from heat and cool for 20 minutes. Add almond or jojoba oil and a pure organic essential oil of your liking (check it's one that can be used during pregnancy).

When the oils start to solidify use an electric mixer to mix until a thick butter-like consistency is achieved. Transfer to a glass jar to store.

APPLE CIDER VINEGAR

This isn't a recipe as such, but try using organic apple cider vinegar as an all-natural conditioner and detangler – just water it down with up to 50% water to reduce the strong smell. It also works as a skin toner that helps reduce skin inflammation, and even as a mouthwash.

CLEANERS

Basic, safe cleaning products we can mix at home are just as effective as the chemical mixes found in stores, and come at a fraction of a cost. Here are two quick tips:

USE LESS

Most homes can be cleaned with five basic tools or ingredients: a high quality vacuum, a microfibre towel, white distilled vinegar, baking soda and castile soap.

DIY AND LOOK IN YOUR KITCHEN

Some of the best 'recipes' for cleaners include ingredients you likely already have at home.

SOME BASIC AND EFFECTIVE RECIPES FOR CLEANERS

ALL-PURPOSE CLEANER

I have been using this easy-to-mix all-purpose cleaner for over ten years and it is so safe that even my young children can mix it together and use it. It is perfect for general cleaning.

Ingredients: 50% white distilled vinegar, 50% water, a couple of drops of your favorite organic essential oil (optional – I like tea tree oil or eucalyptus).

Simply mix ingredients to make the quantity you need, and go.

NON-TOXIC OVEN CLEANER

Oven cleaners are some of the most toxic products that exist. It is completely unnecessary to expose yourself to such harmful chemicals when you can make your own effective oven cleaner.

Ingredients: baking soda, water, white vinegar.

Mix equal quantities of vinegar and water in a spray bottle and spray thoroughly inside the oven. In a bowl, make a thick baking soda paste by adding a couple of drops of water mixed with a little bit of white vinegar to the baking soda. Spread the baking soda paste thoroughly throughout the oven and leave to work for 3–4 hours. With a clean cloth (or paper towel), wipe off the baking soda paste.

BATHROOM SCRUB

This recipe works really well for getting rid of soap scum, removing stains, and brightening your tub, tiles and toilet.

Ingredients: baking soda, white distilled vinegar, castile soap (optional).

Sprinkle baking soda on the surface you want to clean. Spray the vinegar – undiluted – on the sides (pour a cup of vinegar on the toilet, after spraying on the sides, for additional removal of lingering smells). Scrub. For heavy soap scum, pre-clean the area with castile soap.

DRAIN CLEANER

No need to buy incredibly toxic drain cleaners. Instead, pour a pot of boiling hot water down your drain, followed by ½ cup baking soda. Then, pour a cup of white vinegar into the drain and allow the mixture to sit for a couple of minutes. When the fizzing has stopped, flush down with 2–3 cups boiling water.

WEEKS 6–9

BABY: At the beginning of the first trimester your baby is an embryo that is rapidly developing. That embryo resembles a tadpole (sorry for the comparison). Rather than the typical fruit and vegetable scales that are often used to explain the size of a growing baby, we thought we'd go with animals – so get ready to compare your baby to joeys and rabbits. We'll have you dreaming about your own litter of golden retrievers in no time!

Between weeks 5 and 9 your baby's heart will start beating, and you may even be able to hear the heartbeat at your medical check or an early ultrasound. When your baby is approximately the size of a ladybird, arm and leg buds appear and your baby's face begins to form. If you need a moment to take that in, we get it: it is mind blowing how much happens in this first trimester! By the end of the ninth week your embryo will look the same regardless of whether it's a girl or a boy, but this is actually the time when the baby's genitals and reproductive organs begin to develop.

MAMA: Knowing all of this, how are you actually feeling? Some women begin to experience nausea right away, or feel more and more tired during this time – every woman is different. We deliberately avoid the term 'morning sickness' because for us it never actually happened in the morning. With some pregnancies we felt nausea all day long, and with others we felt it in the evening, or if we didn't have enough water.

TIPS FOR EASING NAUSEA[6]

- Eat smaller meals more often. Missing meals can make nausea worse.
- Avoid large drinks. Instead, have frequent small drinks between meals.
- Limit fatty, spicy and fried foods.

↘ Be aware that food has a stronger odour or smell when it is heated, which may make nausea worse. If possible, have other people help with cooking, or prepare your food at the times of the day when you feel better.

↘ Try eating a dry biscuit before you get out of bed in the morning.

↘ Eat a healthy snack before you go to bed at night. This might include fruit (fresh, tinned or dried), crackers with hard cheese or yoghurt.

↘ Try ginger tablets, dry ginger ale, peppermint tea or ginger tea (put 3 or 4 slices of fresh ginger in hot water for 5 minutes).

↘ Avoid foods if their taste, smell or appearance makes you feel sick.

The most important thing is to figure out what works for you. Trust your body, and pay attention to what you need. We dealt with our nausea in many different ways, but making sure you are hydrated and are eating nutritious meals and snacks can help you stay ahead of it. If your sickness is more severe and you feel you are dehydrated and losing more nutrients than you are taking in, always check with your care provider, as there are medicines out there that can help.

You also may experience the need to pee more often, even this early on. Most people think this is because the growing baby is pushing on your bladder, but it's actually thanks to your increasing uterine size and hormonal changes causing increased bodily fluid levels and increased blood flow to your pelvic area. Your kidneys will also work harder to rid your body of waste, so this urge will come to you more often than you're used to. Basically, you become a poop machine, and oh my lord the gas! Yes, for any men reading this book, women DO actually fart; but when you're pregnant you crush toots like it's your job. You could win medals for the duration and volume of your flatulence (though sadly no one seems to be handing those out . . .).

Getting back to business, we know this span of time between doctors' visits can feel daunting, so make sure to check in with yourself. Have you started that journal yet? It will probably help to get thoughts down on paper and bring some equilibrium back to this very busy first trimester. We loved documenting our pregnancies on the Sprout Pregnancy tracker app.

You can expect more poop, more vomit and even more leaks later down the pregnancy line! What a delightful way to get acquainted with the full spectrum of bodily functions before being thrust into funky fluidsville with your little darling when they arrive earth side . . .

WEEKS 10–13

BABY: When your baby is around 11 weeks gestational age they transition from an embryo to a fetus and are about the size of a hummingbird. Your baby will be kicking, dancing and moving around in your uterus, possibly even sucking their thumb, without you even knowing it. Twelve weeks after your last period your fetus is fully formed and their sex organs are well developed. Nails and fingerprints are beginning to form, and by 14 weeks your baby's eyelids will cover their eyes.

MAMA: Even though you won't feel these movements and changes in your baby yet, you may start to see a difference in your own body and appearance. Your tummy may feel bloated or, if you're an early show-er like we were, you may see a change in the shape of your stomach. Your breasts will most likely feel tender and will also start to grow (this part is kind of fun for those of us who always wondered what it would be like to have larger boobs!).

You will have a number of check-ups and tests with your care provider during the first fourteen weeks. If anything ever comes up that makes you feel uncomfortable, or if you see spotting or bleeding, don't hesitate to call your care provider for reassurance.

Boy or girl? That is the question! Or perhaps a better question is, *Do you want to know?* If you're anything like us, you'll want to know your baby's biological sex as soon as humanly possible, but of course, you might enjoy the prospect of a surprise. There are arguments for both!

For some people this will dictate the names they choose, what the baby wears and nursery themes, among other things. Others simply enjoy knowing the sex of their baby and find it to help with the bonding experience.

If you choose to find out the gender and want to share the news with your loved ones, there are so many cute, fun and thrilling ways for the reveal to happen. One option is to have your sonographer write down the gender and seal it in an envelope. You can then give this envelope to a baker, who will fill the inside of a cake with either a pink or blue filling. When you cut it open, voila – the sweet surprise awaits! If you like the cake idea but aren't keen on stereotypical pink and blue, why not choose the parents' favourite cake flavours as the way to determine the sex, such as chocolate vs vanilla? Another cute idea is to take the sealed envelope to a party store and have them fill a helium balloon with coloured confetti. When you pop the balloon, everyone gets showered with excitement!

Often when families decide to keep the gender a secret it is because they love the idea of the ultimate surprise at the moment of birth. Many people cherish this special moment with their partners. Plus, who doesn't love brainstorming a whole lot of different names that could be suitable for any gender? Why not start a baby pool for family and friends to take gender guesses? This is a sweet way to get everyone involved and to ensure maximum anticipation.

When we had our first babies you couldn't find out the gender until around weeks 18–20 with an ultrasound (and a definitive 'Yep, that's a penis!' from the technician). Some countries (including Australia) now offer an early blood test at around 10 weeks, called a non-invasive prenatal test (NIPT). The NIPT analyses genetic information, including biological sex, contained in fetal DNA that passes into the mother's bloodstream to screen for a number of abnormalities. This test is primarily prescribed to screen for Down syndrome so if this is something you would prefer not to test, ask your care provider to explain everything that is checked. If your care provider doesn't offer NIPTs, this test is also offered in many private centres, but unfortunately in Australia it is not covered by Medicare or private health insurance, and can cost around $400 or more. You must ensure you are very clear with your clinic about whether you want the sex of the baby to be disclosed to you.

Sarah: The NIPT test wasn't available when I was pregnant with my son so I had to wait until 18 weeks to learn the gender. When I fell pregnant with my daughter I asked my doctor every week if it was time for the NIPT – I couldn't wait to find out!

EXPECTATIONS

Expectations that come up around this topic can be a funny thing. Some women (and indeed their partners) have an idea of whether they want a boy or a girl and feel very strongly about what they think they are having, while others feel content with either sex and just want a healthy baby (let's be honest, we all want a healthy baby!). Finding out that your baby's sex is different from what you desired or expected can lead to a complicated mash-up of sadness, disappointment or even grief, as well as shame and embarrassment about your emotions. Such 'taboo' feelings often aren't discussed or shared, leading parents to feel isolated in their experiences. But we believe there should be more acknowledgement and judgement-free discussion of this feeling of disappointment to help parents move through it. For most who experience them, the feelings are fleeting – as soon as that little babe is in your arms, their uniqueness and spirit take centre stage regardless of their biological sex.

Teresa: I really wanted a daughter first and so did Mark, who already had a son. When we were told 'boy', I remember my irrational pregnancy brain thinking, I wonder if Mark will still think the baby is special because he already has a son? My worries only lasted a couple of days, though, before the excitement came flooding in about having a little boy and developing our own mama/son bond. Once Bodhi was in my arms I couldn't imagine anyone else but him: he was my dream babe! When Forest came along, I felt so elated that I had two little boys – I was content being in the 'boys-only mamas club' – but then sensed a strange pressure from other people with their relentless comments about trying for a girl next. It had an effect, though – I started longing for a girl, and Mark really wanted a daughter, too. So, when we found out third time around that it was Poet in there, we both cried with joy and shock. Mark commented that she felt really different to him after all the boys, but to me she felt just as beautiful and special as my sons – she was only different in the sense that she was her own person, someone who is not defined by her gender and fits perfectly into her family whoever she may be. I realise now that the longing that other people projected onto me was illusory – what I actually desired was another unique, healthy child to love and that's what I was lucky to receive.

Sarah: I really wanted a boy when I had my first and I ended up having Wyatt! I was over the moon. With my second I felt good about having either a boy or a girl as I was just so grateful to be pregnant again. The moment I got the call from the nurse saying I was expecting a girl, I burst into tears. I was shocked and thrilled – honestly, I don't think I'd realised how much I wanted to have a little girl in my life.

SECOND TRIMESTER

Welcome to the second trimester. Hallelujah! Goodbye pukesville, hello cute baby bump. Some people say this is when the heavy clouds of exhaustion and the I-can't-get-outta-bed feelings begin to lift, and slowly but surely little energy-filled bubbles of light start floating your way.

> **Sarah:** With both of my pregnancies, during the first trimester I felt very tired, body temperature cold, nauseated and on edge. I tried to keep it together but most of the time I just wanted to curl up in a blanket and take naps while sipping on ginger tea and eating crackers. The moment that fourteenth week rolled around I felt like a fog began to lift, as if the world was a bit grey until 14 weeks and then all of a sudden it transformed into rainbow sparkles.

This isn't the case for everyone, so don't feel concerned if the timeline is different for you. It's always good to let your care provider know how you are feeling at your check-ups. If anything comes up that concerns you, don't hesitate to reach out. We called our midwives and doctors so many times to ask questions and try to alleviate the stress of too much internet research. At some point we each had to reevaluate our relationship with the internet and rely more heavily on our care providers and our own natural intuition. A simple phone call is so much more reassuring!

WEEKS 14—16

BABY: At around 14 weeks your baby is about the size of a yellow canary and begins to develop hair all over their body, called lanugo. At 15 weeks they will begin to hear. We feel it is never too early to start talking to your baby – they will learn your voice and this will comfort them when they arrive earth side. Your baby may start to hiccup as they are now developing a precursor to breathing – at some stage you will feel when the hiccups are happening and may even see your belly jiggle. Male babies start to make testosterone and female babies start making eggs in their tiny ovaries (these are the eggs that could turn out to be your grandchildren – eek!).

MAMA: An advantage to this new trimester is that your sex drive may begin to increase. The experts say this is due to increased blood flow to the pelvis and pregnancy hormones. Don't worry if this doesn't happen, however – not all women experience this change. You may also experience increased vaginal discharge (we told you we were talking goop!). This is totally normal, and may require more frequent undie changes or a panty liner. The discharge is caused by those same pregnancy hormones that increase blood flow to your vaginal tissues. Although it can be a bit uncomfortable at times, this increase will actually nourish your stretching and changing tissues. If your discharge has an odour or if you experience burning, swelling, redness or tenderness, call your care provider.

Sarah: When I fell pregnant with my first baby, I was seeing an OB-GYN I had seen for years. I never felt fully comfortable with her cold bedside manner but I knew she was a good doctor. Not being from California it felt a bit overwhelming to seek out someone new, and although my instinct was telling me she wasn't the right fit for me I stayed put. Around 14 weeks pregnant I hurt my rib during a coughing fit and a friend recommended a prenatal chiropractor she was seeing to give me an adjustment – it was Dr Berlin at the Berlin Wellness Center (who you heard from in Chapter 1). The rest of my pregnancy changed completely on meeting and talking with him during that 45-minute session. I shared my concerns about my previous doctor and he offered lots of contacts and friends of his in the birth world for me to talk to. About two weeks later I found myself with a doula (more on these below) and a midwife and had made the decision that I wanted to birth my baby at home.

BABY: This is about the time when fruit comparison lovers would say that your baby is the size of a pear, but we will tell you they are the size of chipmunk. Your baby's body will grow more now, so your ultrasound images will look more baby-like and less reptilian. During this time, you may begin to feel your baby moving. This may be very subtle at first, perhaps just a flutter low below your belly button.

> **Teresa:** I felt Bodhi kick for the first time when I was on the set of a movie I was shooting called *Kill Me Three Times*. It was a particularly violent scene and I remember sitting down between takes for a breather and pop! It felt as though a popcorn kernel had popped in my belly, a light flick. I was 19 weeks along. I ran around asking every woman on the set who had children whether I had just felt the baby kick. They said yes and smiled at the giddiness of a young first-time mother basking in the magic of growing a baby.

Sarah: The first time I felt Wyatt moving inside of me I was driving. I wondered if it was gas bubbles, but it felt different. The only way I could figure out how to describe it was by saying it felt like someone was blowing raspberries on the inside of my stomach.

You may not recognise it when it first happens, but those movements will get stronger and more defined, and eventually you will find yourself staring at your stomach waiting to see a kick or a high five.

By week twenty your baby's skin is covered in a white greasy substance called vernix. Vernix is a white, cheese-like, waxy protective substance on the outside of a newborn's skin. In hospitals some nurses have been known to wipe it away and clean your baby after birth, but it's a biofilm that the body creates, and it is moisturising for babies' skin, so you may prefer to rub it in instead of wiping it off.

You are now halfway through your pregnancy. Between weeks 18 and 20 your care provider might offer you an ultrasound scan to check for abnormalities. You can ask your care provider about this ahead of time so you have a better understanding of what you will see.

MAMA: How are you feeling now? Are your cravings amping up? Do you have energy?

SLEEP

If you are having trouble sleeping or are uncomfortable when you sleep, there are lots of amazing pregnancy pillows available. Alternatively, you could try using extra pillows on your bed. Some pregnant women feel hotter when they sleep, so they opt to sleep with just a sheet and use a fan to keep cool. Frequent urination at night can affect sleep, too, but this is almost impossible to control, unfortunately. Just try to stay hydrated and remember, now is a great time to get little naps in during the day if you can.

Sleeping on your back is not recommended as it can cause lower back pain and shortness of breath. The entire weight of your uterus and baby is pressing on your organs and veins, which in turn can reduce blood flow to both you and the baby. Sleeping on your side is best to increase blood flow and nutrients to your growing fetus. This position takes the pressure of the growing weight off your liver, and increases blood flow and circulation to all major organs. If you are not normally a side sleeper this can be very uncomfortable. Try putting a pillow between your knees to help support your lower back. You can also hug a pillow with your arms to relieve pressure on your shoulders. We loved using the Leachco Snoogle Total Body Pillow.

BABY: Your baby is the size of a puffin and is now sleeping and waking – but not necessarily at the same time as you. Try to notice when your baby is moving around. Do you feel the dance party start when you lie down at night? Or maybe your baby starts moving in the morning, right after you have breakfast. Some women find when they are walking around a lot, hiking or exercising, that they don't feel baby as much, but when they sit down to rest or lie down to sleep, they feel lots of kicks and movement. This will be different for everyone, so it's good to take note of your baby's movements. You may even see a pattern begin to form, and this will tell you when your baby is sleeping and when they are awake. This is also around the time your baby's tastebuds begin to form. If you eat that spicy chili on your sandwich there is a good chance your baby will taste it.

Sarah: Around this time my husband recorded himself reading the kids' book *Goodnight Moon* to our son and I would play it every night before bed. I wanted my baby to hear and feel comfort from his daddy's voice the same way I knew he would feel comfort from me. Watching him as a newborn, I could see how Eric's voice would calm his body and his tears and I think that familiarity helped their bond strengthen in those early weeks of life.

MAMA: Around 23 weeks pregnant you may start seeing a dark line appear down your stomach. This is called the linea nigra. This line is caused by the same pregnancy hormones (melanocyte-stimulating hormone) made by the placenta that cause your nipples to become darker. Not all women get this line, but it is more common if you have darker skin.

Okay, not exactly a medical term, but it defines very nicely the sharp shooting pain you may experience in your vagina during these weeks. This actually happens at different times in the pregnancy for different women. There are a number of causes of this, from ligament pain or the baby kicking, stretching and hitting a nerve, to bending or moving in a certain way. This feeling should come and go very quickly, but if you experience prolonged pain in your pelvis or vagina always contact your care provider and let them know.

Some women say they feel everything sooner in their second pregnancy, and the 'lightning' you felt shooting up your vagina the first time around, or the pressure against your pubic bone, may arrive much sooner the second time around. This is because your body already knows what's happening and it is preparing you much earlier for the months ahead.

WEEKS 25–28

BABY: Your animal baby is now the size of a potoroo – much bigger than the ladybirds and canaries of a matter of weeks ago. Your baby's nostrils will start to open and they will be taking practice breaths. Your baby's digestive system, brain and lungs are now in place, but will continue to develop between now and birth. By 28 weeks your baby weighs roughly 1 kilogram.

MAMA: You are nearing the end of your second trimester, so now may be a good time to check in with your body and see how you feel. During this time some women experience heartburn and indigestion. You may notice that, thanks to your growing belly, you feel full more quickly when eating. Eating smaller meals and snacks throughout the day will help keep you nourished and control your indigestion.

THIRD TRIMESTER

You're in your third and final trimester! While you probably feel like your body couldn't get any bigger (unbelievably, it will!), things are rapidly changing. Your mind may keep wandering to the impending birth. What will your baby look like? How will you know when you're in labour? What the heck's a mucus plug?! This trimester brings all things awesome, gnarly and utterly incredible!

WEEKS 29–32

BABY: Your baby is plumping up. Over the next eleven weeks they will double and possibly triple their weight to be around 1.7 kilograms. This is a good time to start paying attention to your baby's kicks and movements and make a mental note of them – they call this 'kick counting'. If any maternal perception of decrease in frequency or strength of fetal movements (which includes dancing, turning and high fives), advise your care provider as soon as possible.

MAMA: Now is a good time to start thinking about your labour and delivery preferences. We advocate for *informed* birth, so let's consider some of the options available.

BIRTH PREFERENCES

Maybe you haven't thought this far ahead yet, or maybe you already know that you want to have a hospital birth with an epidural or a caesarean section. You may have discussed your home birth with your midwife or your birth centre birth with your care provider. You may not want to think about birth until the day it comes, or maybe you don't want to overthink it. But when it comes to birth, we believe knowledge is power, so take some time out during these few weeks to wrap your head around your baby's exit strategy!

There are so many great resources out there to help you make an informed decision about how and where to birth your baby. Only your doctor will know your individual situation, of course, but we really enjoyed these additional resources:

- *Dr Berlin's Informed Pregnancy* podcast
- *Australian Birth Stories* podcast
- *The Business of Being Born* (US-focused but fascinating)
- *Birth Story: Ina May Gaskin and The Farm Midwives*

Teresa: I listened religiously to Sarah Walker's *Australian Birth Stories* podcast during my second and third pregnancies. I love that it's unbiased and inclusive of all experiences. Sarah asks her guests thought-provoking questions about their conception journey, pregnancy, birth stories and postpartum experiences. It really helps to hear firsthand from mamas about their different choices and what worked for them, and I've shared my own stories on there, too.

WHERE

How do you see your birth? Do you love the idea of having a water birth at home? Would you feel more comfortable in a hospital setting with some candles and music? If you haven't already decided on where you will have your baby, now would be a good time to discuss this with your chosen care provider. If you aren't sure how you feel about it yet, that is totally fine! Sometimes our decisions become clearer when we learn more about our options. Take this time to educate yourself on the places you can have an assisted birth (if that is what you are looking for) in your city or town. That knowledge may change how you feel about your birthing options.

It is also important to take into consideration the costs involved. If you choose to use the Australian public health care system, then nearly all costs are covered. The costs of giving birth in a private hospital vary, but can be anywhere between

$2000 and $10 000. If you have a low-risk pregnancy with no complications you may be a good candidate for home birth. In Australia, you can have a home birth either with a private midwife ($3500–$6000), or through a publicly funded home birth program (up to $1500).[7]

WHO WITH: CHOOSING YOUR BIRTH TEAM

So, you love your midwife, your doctor is a rockstar and your partner didn't fall asleep in those classes with you – yep, you're feeling quietly confident about your little crew. By this point in life you probably know yourself pretty well, too, and can envision whether giving birth in a room full of people would be helpful or way too much. Either way, it can be a great idea (if you feel comfortable) to have at least one other person besides your birth partner and medical care providers attending your birth to help support you and/or your partner. You never know how you might feel when the day finally arrives, so having a friend, family member or doula (see below) on standby to fetch snacks, take photos, grab anything you forgot or even just hold your hand and fan you could prove to be a real practical and emotional aid.

A DOULA

Sarah: What's a doula? I remember wondering this myself when I found out I was pregnant. I was under the impression doulas could deliver babies and I wondered why you would have both a doula and a care provider.

Doulas do not in fact deliver babies – they are birth workers who can take on many different roles in your pregnancy and delivery. The primary job of a doula is to mother the mother – they're there to support you and your partner and offer guidance and encouragement. You do not have to be certified to call yourself a doula, but there are certified doulas. You can get a DONA international certified doula who has been trained and has attended numerous births. They use their knowledge, training and passion to help the mama get through her birthing day. From special light touch massage techniques, working with a rebozo scarf and sound healing (yup, Teresa had one of those kinds of doulas at her first birth!) to understanding positions and natural pain relief techniques, using powerful affirmations and essential oils and playing great music, they are there with one goal in mind: to be an incredibly supportive force for the birthing mama. We both leaned heavily on our doulas, and that meant our husbands were able to hold us in all the ways they needed to without needing to know all the special 'tips, tricks and techniques' – there was someone else there with lots of experience to do that. Doulas are also fabulous at helping a mother voice her feelings or concerns: whether it's asking the right questions of the doctor or midwife, knowing the birth plan and the mother's choices back to front or just helping the mama to process any necessary changes to the plan, during a very vulnerable time doulas will help you advocate for yourself. So if you're considering jumping on the doula bandwagon, we'd say a resounding yes!

Doulas are professionals trained and experienced in supporting both mother and partner during pregnancy, childbirth and postpartum by providing non-biased, evidence-based information as well as physical and emotional support. Research and scientific evidence indicates that the use of birth doulas can improve physical and emotional health outcomes such as shorter labours, lower C-section rates, higher breastfeeding rates and higher birth satisfaction scores by mothers. Many hospitals are starting doula programs, making doulas part of their staff and care team. Doulas have been endorsed by the American College of Obstetricians and Gynecologists (ACOG), the most prestigious and respected obstetrical medical association.

There are more than 80 companies and organisations training doulas today and if seeking one, it is important to ensure they have received proper training both in skills to support parents and in how to collaborate with medical birth professionals such as obstetricians, pediatricians, midwives and nurses.

– ANA PAULA MARKEL, BIRTH DOULA TRAINER AND FORMER PRESIDENT OF DONA INTERNATIONAL

FRIENDS

If you decide you want someone else a little more familiar to you at your birth, why don't you consider asking one or more of your best friends? If they've given birth before themselves, they'll be another person in the room who knows you well and gets what you're going through; they've been there, and it can be comforting to know that. Friends who don't have kids are hugely valuable, too – the pure fact that they know you so well means they may know what song to play and when, they'll know exactly what to say if you're having doubts and they'll know how to make you laugh. Having your friends in the room can be such a special bonding experience, and an immeasurable help on your birthing day.

> **Teresa:** I had a doula with my first birth in the USA, then with my second and third births in Australia, I chose my bestie Kat to act as my doula. She has a background as a paramedic and is very well equipped with medical knowledge. She is also an advocate for natural, low-intervention births if that is the mother's wish. I knew she would be my voice and it also brought the added bonus of an extra set of eyes if anything was to turn into an emergency. I feel utterly safe in her hands, and our 25 years of best friendship means that she just knows me so well and understands what I need in the different moments.

FAMILY

This is an interesting one! Your mother, sister, father or parents-in-law can make wonderful members of your birth team, but parents and siblings can sometimes be so invested in you and your baby's health and wellbeing that just seeing you go through the mentally and physically challenging experience of labour can make them worried. The last thing you need is to be thinking about someone else's feelings. If you believe your mum or sister has what it takes to be that fierce guiding light for you, cheering you on without getting stressed or anxious, then go for it. Remember that your birthing space has to feel safe and completely sacred, so anyone's tense energy (even if it comes with the best intentions) is likely to have an impact on you. You just want to focus on the task at hand and feel completely uninhibited (and that's why many of the in-laws get crossed off the list!).

Teresa: For my first two births I decided not to have my mum present in the room. With Poet's birth she really wanted to be there to watch her granddaughter being born. My main hesitation was that my beautiful mum is such a worry wart! But I thought about it a lot and realised what a remarkable experience it would be for her, so I prepped her long in advance about the birth room being a 'resting worry face free space' – that meant no whipping out her rosary beads and rocking back and forth in distress! And I gotta tell you, she was nothing but INCREDIBLE on the day: so loving, gentle, sweet, trusting and gloriously positive and happy. I only now wish I had allowed her to be there at Forest's birth too! Her presence during Poet's birth was one of the highlights for me.

A PHOTOGRAPHER

Consider whether you'd like to have your birth documented – some women later feel sad or regretful about not having enough good-quality photos of their births. It's best not to rely on your partner to take happy snaps, as there'll be so much going on! If you decide to go down this route, interview a birth photographer, just as you would a doula, to get a sense of their personality, and check out their portfolio to see if their work resonates with you. The birthing room needs to be airtight, energy-wise, so if you don't find a professional who you click with, perhaps ask a friend to take on photographer duty. We were each other's photographers at each of our first births and Gemma Pranita, who photographed us for this book, was Teresa's photographer for Poet's birth and her first twenty-four hours earth side.

BIRTH TEAM ROLES

Aside from a doula, everyone else will probably be wondering how they can help on the day. It's a good idea to send an email to your team when you're around 35 weeks so it's all fresh in their minds. In your email, include all the important information, including your birth plan (see below), a plan of attack on the day (who is meeting where, where your other kids are going if you have any, who is bringing what, etc.), addresses, phone numbers of the hospital, and contact details of everyone in the birth support team. Perhaps allocate a few jobs to them. For example:

- Claire is in charge of ensuring the playlist is going and reminding me of my affirmations.
- Kat can ensure I'm sipping water after each contraction (keeping hydrated actually lessens the intensity of the waves).
- Sarah, please remind me to pee every hour (again, an empty bladder lessens the intensity of contractions).

Giving your team specific information to read through will undoubtedly be helpful, and provides them with a fallback plan if they get stuck and aren't sure how else they can help.

HOW: DO YOU NEED A BIRTH PLAN?

You may have heard your friends, doula or care provider talk about a birth plan. It's great to have one written out so that on birthing day, everyone assisting you is well aware of your preferences. It doesn't need to be anything formal but it's worth having on hand, with some families sticking it up on the hospital room wall. You can include things like:

- I would like to have a water birth.
- Please keep the room warm and dimly lit.
- No students or unnecessary extra staff in the room.
- Do not offer me pain relief.
- Only give me pain relief after I've requested it on three separate occasions (or gimme the damn drugs as soon as humanly possible!!!).
- I would like to birth in the position of my choice.
- No directed pushing.
- My husband and I would like to lift the baby out.
- I'd like immediate skin on skin contact with my baby after birth.
- Do not cut my baby's cord until the cord has stopped pulsating.
- Do baby's checks while baby is on my body and only remove them if medically necessary.
- After birth please leave the vernix on my baby's body.
- I want to breastfeed as soon as possible after baby's birth.
- No tests to be performed or medication to be administered to my baby without my and my partner's prior consent unless in an emergency.

Sarah: I found a midwife and a doula with my first baby and spent a lot of time discussing my thoughts around birth and what I hoped for. I asked lots of questions and felt confident that I didn't need to fill out a birth plan. With my second baby I found an OB-GYN who I loved, and planned to have a hospital birth. My doctor was very supportive of my natural birth preferences for labour and delivery, so I did not feel I needed to have a birth plan. That being said, he is a doctor known for memorising birth preferences and sticking to them. It can be so helpful to make one and give it to your care provider just for peace of mind.

Teresa: With my first birth I was using a home birth midwife in LA. She was all for my preferences and actually gave me wonderful, calming suggestions that helped support mama and baby. With my second and third births I chose to birth in Australia with a midwife, Julie Schiller, through the midwifery program in Adelaide at Flinders Hospital. It's a floor in the hospital that is a birth centre and provides the opportunity to have a water birth in a large private birthing room. It's amazing. We spoke about my preference to have a water birth among other things and she jotted the notes down in her book but, being a midwife, Julie's instincts are all about letting the baby and mama work in tandem, with no interventions. So, in this instance, I didn't need to write out a specific birth plan. Julie asked me about what my dream birth would look like and she was there to hold a loving and calm space for me, supporting me through words and encouragement when needed. It was exactly what I wished for.

Your best birth 'plan' might be finding a care provider you feel aligned with and just sitting with them and discussing your birth preferences. Read some positive birth stories (we highly recommend Ina May Gaskin's *Spiritual Midwifery*), and spend some time talking with your partner about the kind of birth you envision. Once you have a clear sense of which direction you want to take, schedule an appointment with your doctor or midwife to chat about your wishes. Check out some sample birth plans to get a better understanding of what questions you may be asked on the day. It's a great way to educate yourself and help you feel more prepared.

If you've decided on a hospital birth with a doctor, we recommend taking the time to write your birth plan. Often in these situations, the doctor will only join you at the end of the birth, and you'll have different midwives – some you haven't met – popping in and out throughout labour. You will want everyone to be on the same page about your preferences. If you have a midwife who will be in the room or at home with you on the day, you may feel comfortable just discussing your birth ideals rather than needing to write it all out.

If a caesarean has been chosen or is necessary, there are many wonderful options available to you, such as having a photographer in the room capturing the birth, having music playing, immediate skin on skin with your baby after they are born, and even being able to see your baby being delivered, watching through a see-through sheet! Talk about your options with your care provider to make sure you have the best possible birth.

It's important to gauge your relationship with your care provider and make sure you are on the same page. You may want to ask them if you need to explain anything to the midwives or birth workers on the day. You can also have your doctor/midwife read through each point of your birth plan and sign it. Ask your partner to stick your birth plan on the wall in the birth room so that anyone who comes in is aware of your choices.

A few final words on planning: it's really important to visualise how you see your birth. You can meditate on it, write out your dream delivery and include your choices in your birth plan. But then the *most* important thing? Let. It. Go. Set your intention for the kind of birth you desire, but then make sure you embrace what comes in the moment, as it may not turn out exactly (or even at all) as you planned. Sometimes having expectations can keep you from being present and letting your body, your baby and your chosen care provider guide you. Remember, you have the right to feel supported, nurtured, educated and communicated with in a clear and considerate manner. Planning ahead has lots of advantages, but staying open (in more ways than one!) and sitting in your divine feminine strength is the key to having a more positive birthing experience.

Our midwife gave us a very important tip to help reduce the likelihood of tearing during delivery. Perineal massage is thought to increase muscle and tissue elasticity. It is also said to soften connective tissue during late pregnancy and help prevent perineal trauma and ongoing perineal pain.

To do perineal massage, you gotta get handsy down there! Here's how it works:

- Wash your hands thoroughly (obvs!).
- Insert your thumbs (or any two fingers really) into your vagina, about 2 cm in, and apply light pressure against opposite sides of the opening. Massage up and along the entrance, deepening the stretch at the back portion of the birth canal, down near your rectum. Hold the stretched position for as long as comfortable. Do this massage for 10–15 minutes each day.

WEEKS 33–36

You're on the home stretch now! Speaking of stretch, have you noticed any stretch marks? These occur in many pregnancies, and can range from having a silvery tone to a reddish-purple tinge. We both experienced these in pregnancy, on our breasts and around our belly buttons. There's not much you can do about them. No matter how many oils and creams you religiously rub into your skin, some women are just more prone to stretch marks than others! We look at them as little reminders of our warrior bodies and what they went through to birth our babes.

BABY: At 33 weeks your baby is about the size of an echidna curled up in the uterus, and may be kicking you in the exact same spot every time. You may even be able to see a foot or an elbow pushing the outside of your still-growing belly. Your baby will be practising their breathing, kicking and sucking. Your baby's brain develops at a rapid pace during this time.

MAMA: Have you heard of Braxton Hicks? It's when your uterus begins practising and flexing its muscles to prepare for delivery. Some women feel this as early as 20 weeks, others not until 30+ weeks and some don't experience it at all. Basically, it feels like a tightening that happens from the top of your uterus, spreading down. This will last from fifteen to thirty seconds. Some women experience more Braxton Hicks when they are a little dehydrated, so make sure you stay well hydrated throughout your pregnancy. If your BH are uncomfortable, stop what you are doing and change your position. This is a great opportunity to practise checking in with your body and seeing what it is asking for.

Sarah: When I was pregnant with my son I walked 3 to 5 miles a day, roughly five days a week. I remember in my third trimester thinking I was going into labour as I was walking around the track at UCLA. My body kept telling me to get on all fours on the ground, so I did. That relieved the pressure and the tightening. I called my midwife from this very flattering bent over position as young college athletes ran past me. She told me to stop walking and drink some water. She then explained to me that these were Braxton Hicks contractions, and my body was just practising labour. She also said this was probably happening more because I needed to drink more water.

MORE FLUID TALK

We promised you we'd talk about the mucus plug! This is an amazing grouping of cells and mucus that positions itself in the opening of your uterus during pregnancy, blocking your cervix to protect it from infection. At the end of your pregnancy you will lose your mucus plug, either in parts or all in one go – a key sign that your body is getting ready for labour. You may hear some care providers, doulas or friends refer to this as the 'bloody show'. It can be pink-tinged, brownish,

beige-coloured or white, but not all mucus plugs look the same (and whatever you do, don't go googling images – you don't want that in your brain!).

PACK YOUR HOSPITAL BAG

Only about 5 per cent of babies are born on their actual due date, so it doesn't hurt to have a bag packed and ready to go. Some women want to set up their hospital/birth centre room with things that remind them of home or make them feel more relaxed. You don't want to be racing around grabbing things at the last moment, so sorting this in advance will help you feel more prepared and Zen.

Ideas for your bag:

MAMA

- Battery-powered candles to set the mood you desire
- Crystals (not for everyone, but if they're your thing you don't want to leave them at home)
- Wireless speaker for bluetooth/online playlist
- A pillow or blanket from home, if that makes you feel more comfortable
- Slippers/socks
- PJs and a nightgown or robe
- A few pairs of your sexiest granny undies, preferably black (lots of leaky flow during the postpartum period)
- Maternity pads
- A swimsuit for you and your partner for the shower/birthing tub if you don't want to be nude
- A change or two of cosy clothes for your postpartum stay
- Coconut oil for your partner or care provider to use on your perineum during delivery

- TENS machine (optional electronic pain relief tool)
- A sock tied with two tennis balls inside (another great pain relief tool for back labour)
- Scented cold flannels (keep them wet in the fridge until go time!)
- Snacks for Mum/Dad
- Toiletries
- Phone charger

BABY

- A couple of receiving blankets
- One or two onesies
- An outfit to go home in
- Spare outfit in case of the first one getting messy!
- A swaddle
- Nappies
- A hat
- Soft cloths to wipe their little sensitive bottom
- Car seat!

If this baby isn't your first, this would be a great time to make a plan for your other children. Do you want your kids there while you are in labour or would you prefer to have a babysitter or family member stay with your kids? It's never too early to put this plan into place.

Teresa: My favourite part of my labour with Poet was that both my boys were there. Bodhi brought me water with a straw, stroked my head, gave me light touch massage and told me 'You're so strong, Mama, the strongest!' Forest woke up right as Poet was being born and one of my favourite moments was seeing both of their big smiles when she came out. Bodhi told me that it was the best day of his life! He even cut the cord by himself and felt very proud about it. I'd prepped Bodhi and Forest by showing them other water birth videos, and had their godmother present to support them. I highly recommend including your children if you feel it would be a positive experience for you.

Sarah: When I had my daughter Esmé I really wanted my son Wyatt to be there. I was going to have a natural hospital birth, so I asked the hospital for the rules about having a sibling in the room. They said that most women don't have other children there, but they can't kick them out if you bring them on the day. My son was sleeping when I left for the hospital that morning but he came for the last hour of his sister's birth and he cheered me on, sang songs and made me feel so good as he welcomed his baby sister earth side.

WEEKS 37–40

BABY: Your baby is considered full-term at 37 weeks, and on average weighs around 3–4 kilograms. Reaching full term is such a good feeling after months of growing your little love! Your baby is now producing meconium, a sticky green substance that contains the waste from amniotic fluid and will be your baby's first poo.

MAMA: At some point during these weeks your baby will move further down into your pelvis. This is called being 'engaged'. Some babies don't engage this early on, but you may notice your belly drop one day, and you may feel more pressure on your pubic bone. Oh, and that exciting lightning crotch often rears its ugly head in these last few weeks. Your walk may now have turned into a full-blown waddle, and you probably haven't seen your vagina in a *very* long time!

So how are you feeling? Are you rushing around trying to fix up a room for baby or finish your last bits of work? We highly suggest you take these last few weeks to rest, meditate, listen to hypnobirthing techniques or watch birth videos. Take baths! Our favourite thing to do was to read Ina May books in between naps and snacks and listen to birth stories from Sophie Walker's *Australian Birth Stories* podcast. This is such a special time to rest your body and your mind before your baby arrives.

WEEKS 41–42

Most women will go into labour between 37 and 42 weeks. If you haven't gone into labour yet, your care provider will monitor you and your baby more frequently to make sure your baby is doing okay. Amniotic fluid levels are lower now, so it is important to stay hydrated and get lots of rest. If you are feeling anxious about meeting your new little love, ask your care provider if there are things you can do to help your body along.

Teresa: I've gone over my 'guess date' with my last two pregnancies. I have to say it doesn't get easier for me! With Forest I gave birth at 40 weeks + 5 days and with Poet I was 40 weeks + 2 days. The days leading up to the births I was trying all the natural induction methods: red raspberry leaf tea, induction massage, acupuncture, hiking, figures of eight on the birth ball, sex, spicy food. ALL THE THINGS! Finally I just realised that my babes had their own divine timing and I let go of trying to control when they were joining us. All babies come out eventually, so I just had to embrace that. The hardest part was navigating everyone else's questions, expectations and impatience!

You've made it, ladies! You've waddled your way to the very end, navigated all the colours of the rainbow, been through the ebbs and flows, felt the pangs of tiredness, fear, despair, hope, excitement and giddiness, and you are *just about to meet your baby*. It's time to move on to all things birth. Like pregnancy, this is a completely unique experience with its own surprises, challenges and magic.

ZEN NOTES

- Sharing the news with those closest to you can be so exciting! Figure out who you'd like to be in the know from the start, and who won't find out until you announce your pregnancy publicly.

- Get familiar with the nutrients you'll need throughout pregnancy and which foods and drinks to avoid.

- Journal your progress! You will never regret writing down the memories of these special days.

- Make movement a priority! Take a walk with your partner and soak up some vitamin D.

- Remove any toxic chemicals from your home.

- Take naps and listen to your body. If your body says you need to rest, listen!

- Figure out where you want to have your baby and how. Know your options so you can inform those around you about how you want the 'birth' day to go down.

- Choose an amazing, loving and supportive team to attend your birth.

- Put together your hospital/birthing centre bag and then sit back, relax and know that you will soon be holding your sweet beautiful bubs in your arms.

BIRTHING POWER

FOUR

Welcome to your birthing day! You've made it to one of the most anticipated moments of a mother's life. Childbirth can bring all sorts of emotions: excitement, happiness, fear, anxiety and that thank-god-this-pregnancy-is-almost-done relief! All these feelings are valid and warranted – no matter how many births you've had, each one is unique. Just as we discussed in Chapter 3, visualise how you see your birth going, meditate on it, write out your dream delivery, make sure you're well versed in your birth plan, and then Let It Go. There is no way to know how your birth is going to unfold, no matter how much preparation and dreaming you've done. Now is the time to release expectations and be open (in more ways than one!) to your baby's unique birth story.

When it comes to navigating birth, there are numerous techniques and schools of thought (e.g. hypnobirthing, the Bradley method, Lamaze, Calm Birth etc.). We suggest doing all the research you can to work out which style resonates with you. In this chapter we'll discuss a smash-up of methods, bits and bobs we've pulled from personal experience, books we've read, documentaries we've watched and our own philosophies developed through the five births we've experienced between us. Go get 'em, Mama!

THE BEGINNING OF LABOUR

HOW TO KNOW YOU'RE GOING INTO LABOUR

The start of labour is very different for each woman, but here are some telltale signs that baby is fully cooked and labour is just around the corner:

- Cramps
- Frequent contractions increasing in strength and length
- A 'bloody show' (a small amount of pinky or blood-tinged mucus at the end of pregnancy; this signals that you've lost your mucus plug)
- Water breaking
- Diarrhoea
- The sensation of baby dropping, also known as the baby 'engaging' – it means bub has moved down into your pelvis
- An increase in vaginal discharge
- Braxton Hicks contractions
- Dull pain in your lower back
- Overwhelming emotions
- Feelings of nesting (cleaning/sorting/planning)

Teresa: With Poet's birth I could have sworn I was in labour the whole week before I actually gave birth. I'd be feeling contractions in the morning, which would be consistent, but then they would peter out at night time. I'd send the 'I think it's happening!' text to my birth team and then have to send a sheepish 'false alarm' text later that day. The stop/start pattern was just how that labour went, and was very different from my previous labours.

LABOUR: THINGS THAT HELPED US

Between us we have journeyed a whole gamut of birth experiences: a home birth transfer, shoulder dystocia, cervical lips, stalled labour, water births, home birth, hospital births, birth centre births, tears, retained placenta, back labour and many things in between. There are a multitude of unknowns when it comes to birth, but the approaches and methods we discuss below have aided us in our quest to have smoother second and third births and we hope will give you some extra tips for your first and potentially subsequent births.

There are three stages of labour. The first is the process of your cervix opening up through contractions. This stage consists of the early or latent phase of labour (dilation of the cervix up to 3 centimetres), active labour (3 or 4 to 7 centimetres dilation) and the transitional phase of labour (7 to 10 centimetres dilation). By this point your baby is almost ready to be pushed out and you are reaching full dilation. The transitional phase, while often described as the most intense period of labour, typically lasts only a short period of time, and the silver lining is knowing that you are so close to meeting your baby!

The second stage of labour begins once your cervix is fully dilated to 10 centimetres. This stage is completed once you have pushed your baby out. The third stage of labour is birthing the placenta and membranes. Generally, your placenta will feel a whole lot easier to push out than your baby. The placenta usually comes out within an hour of giving birth – all that skin-on-skin, cuddling and oxytocin release helps separate the placenta from your uterine wall, ready for exit. Your vaginal birth is now complete!

Teresa: When it came to my third experience of giving birth I took my knowledge and previous experiences and managed to get that high, transcendent feeling that I had read about women experiencing in Ina May Gaskin's *Spiritual Midwifery*. I used a lot of what I'd read in that book, including laughter, smiling, which released endorphins, taking the edge off – this is something that Ina talks a lot about. I used words like 'yes', 'thank you' and 'stretch'. I danced and spiralled my hips, hung over birth balls, rocked on my hands and knees, kept things really positive and whenever I felt fear arise or thought 'Wow, these are really intense,' I would try and lean into the feeling instead of tensing up and trying to run away from it. Whenever I tightened up, I felt like the contractions were too strong for me, but when I relaxed and rode them one by one using the many techniques I knew about, I found it all so manageable, and even enjoyable (at times!).

LABOUR POSITIONS

As you'll soon learn, birth has its ebbs and flows – one position might feel soothing at one point and then something completely different might bring comfort at another time. Most women will use a mixture of different positions during labour. Often your body will tell you how it wants to be positioned, but it's good to be equipped with numerous possible movements that can help alleviate discomfort. It's also a wise idea to word your birth partner up on these positions, so that on the day they can help you remember your options. Listen to your body, it will guide you to work out what will feel best for you. These suggestions are what worked for us.

HANDS AND KNEES

This is an amazing position to be in for labour and we utilised it a lot while rolling and moving our hips. The hands and knees position can also help labour advance, while giving you lots of options to play around with movement: rocking forwards, pushing back on your ankles into a squat, resting your head on your hands, kneeling upright and stretching backwards into a light back bend during the peaks, and spiralling your hips around and forwards again. This position can really aid those of us who experience back labour.

Sarah: This was a position I found myself in a lot during my third trimester, as it relieved a lot of pressure I was feeling and allowed my body to relax. I wondered if it would help me during labour, and I actually ended up pushing my son out in this position. After four hours of pushing (and seventeen hours of labour in total), Wyatt had finally started to crown and then his head was out – but his shoulders were stuck. Eric, having read all the same books I had read, said, 'She needs to do the Gaskin manoeuvre.' He was right. My midwife told me to get onto all fours (a position taught worldwide by Ina May Gaskin) so we could get Wyatt out. My doula kicked into some incredible powerful lioness mode and chanted words in my ear to encourage me to push harder and use all the strength I had left. Her words, Eric's voice, Teresa's voice, everyone's presence and the energy in the room was all so strong. I took one powerful breath and pushed with everything I had left inside and finally felt the biggest release. He was out – and way bigger than I'd thought, at 4.44 kilograms and 53 centimetres long!

STANDING

We've used standing periodically during labour. We've stood in the shower, pulling down on overhead bars when necessary, having our partner standing behind us, taking our weight as we leant into them, swaying together. The greatest thing about being in the standing position is how much movement you have: dancing, bending, rolling, stretching, circling. A series of standing movements really relieves pressure and tension, and helps boost your mental stamina.

Teresa: I REALLY utilised standing movements in my third birth. I was holding onto a bar in the shower, rolling and twisting my body in and out of the steamy water, dancing through it, utilising vocalisation, visualisation and movement to help me through the peaks. I was in the shower for about two and a half hours and went from 6–9 cm dilation. It felt like the perfect labour space for me, I loved the water and the freedom to move throughout the contractions.

Sarah: With my second birth, during the transition before pushing began, I couldn't sit, I couldn't lie down – I couldn't do anything but stand. I actually kept visualising a pull-up bar and wanting to hang from it. I searched every corner of the room and bathroom for a way to hang and stretch my body. It was purely instinctual – the baby felt so large coming down.

BIRTH BALL

A birth ball can be a huge help during labour. You can place it in the shower and bounce on it during contractions while the hot water hits you, which feels about as amazing as you can feel during labour. Alternatively, you can kneel on the floor with your upper body collapsed over the top of the ball, rocking from side to side, or you can sit on it bouncing around in circles and swaying your hips to work through the sensations. Your partner can also sit on the ball while you squat in front of them, leaning against it, arms dangled over your partner's legs as they take your weight, working in tandem to help bring your baby down. Let them do some of the heavy lifting, too!

Teresa: Earlier in the week before I gave birth to Bodhi, I had written out signs and put them around the room to remind me of positions and comforts that might help me during labour. One said *Birthing ball in the shower*, and it was seriously like HEAVEN to me. I kept asking, 'Can I please stay here?' (Yes, apparently I managed to stay pretty polite during labour, which I was pleased to hear!)

SIDE LYING

Sometimes during birth, especially longer births, we need to get some rest and utilise positions that help restore energy. Our home-birth midwife suggested Teresa get into the side lying position while labouring with her first baby, since she'd been in labour for 24 hours, much of it in her back, and fatigue had started to set in. Side lying, while not always as comfortable as some of the more active labour positions, can be helpful for muscular relief.

> **Sarah:** I hated side lying but my midwife made me do it for a while, as Wyatt was in a weird position and we were trying to help my body negotiate him out of it. In the end it helped a lot.

DELIVERY POSITIONS

COMMUNITY QUESTION: WHY IS LYING DOWN ON YOUR BACK THE MOST COMMON WAY TO DELIVER BABIES?

Two of the most common positions for delivery are lying flat on your back with your legs apart, or sitting rocked back on your tailbone, so your body is sort of shaped like a C. According to a national survey in the US, around 90 per cent of women who give birth vaginally end up delivering in one of these positions. But there are other positions. Some women give birth lying on their side, squatting, or on their hands and knees.[1]

There's actually no research that suggests that those two most common positions are best for mother or baby – their popularity is thought to be the result of medical convenience, as they give doctors easier access. But these positions can actually tilt the birth canal upwards, meaning the mother is essentially pushing the baby uphill. The most important thing is to work out what feels best for you, in consultation with your care provider.

> **Sarah:** I somehow ended up in this position in both births. I didn't love lying on my back, as I felt it took all my might to push my baby out. I pushed for four hours with my son: in squat position, side lying with a leg in the air, standing and going into a squat, on the toilet, on my back and then finally in the end on hands

and knees. While lying on my back I pushed from an upper part of my body and actually popped a rib out of place. For me, hands and knees or in a squat felt much more productive for the later stages of pushing.

ALTERNATIVE BIRTH POSITIONS

While some women have very positive experiences giving birth on their backs, others struggle with the second stage of labour because this position doesn't make use of gravity to aid the process. Here are a few alternative positions.

HANDS AND KNEES

is the position Teresa gave birth in with her last two pregnancies, at the instruction of her care providers. It is one of two optimal positions for birthing that use gravity. Birthing on hands and knees takes the pressure off both the perineum and urethra, lessening the chance of tearing. It's also beneficial for birthing a large baby.

SQUATTING

is another wonderful way to birth your baby. It takes the natural pull of gravity and makes the passageway easier for your baby to manoeuvre through. Women have birthed in this very natural and instinctive position for thousands of years.

STANDING

is one of the most underused birth positions, although it's starting to gain popularity. It utilises gravity to help bring the babe out swiftly. We have seen many birth videos of women remaining in the standing position in the shower while birthing their baby, and often women can be supported in this upright position by their partner or doula. It also gives her great access to catch the baby and bring them up to her chest.

If you've had an epidural, especially if it's a stronger dose and you don't have any sensations in your lower half, birthing on your back may be your only option. A half-strength epidural or a 'walking epidural', on the other hand, should enable you to be supported in a squatting or hands and knees position. This is something you should ask about in advance, as some hospitals have a policy about lying down for delivery. We would recommend finding a doctor and/or hospital that allows you to birth in the position you wish to.

TECHNIQUES WE USED FOR PUSHING AND PREVENTING TEARING

We both devoured Ina May Gaskin's books *Spiritual Midwifery* and *Ina May's Guide to Childbirth*. We wanted to be informed in every way, and her books gave us so many amazing suggestions and techniques, and left us feeling very empowered. Many of the things we discuss below are derived from Ina May's philosophy, and we really recommend reading up on them further with her as your expert guide.

COMMUNITY QUESTION: WHAT DOES PUSHING FEEL LIKE?

Obviously, everyone experiences the second stage of labour differently: for some it brings welcome relief from the constant waves of contractions experienced during labour, while others prefer riding the contractions or 'rushes', as Ina describes them. Some women experience a feeling of pressure as the body intuitively starts bearing down (another term for pushing) to dispel the baby. Other women don't feel the urge to push (this was Teresa's experience with her first labour). This sometimes has to do with the baby's position or the use of strong pain relief – the bear down technique (explained more below) is necessary for those who may not have feeling in their pelvic floor due to an epidural and are pushing from a lying down position. Either way, that baby is coming out and you want to have some semblance of an idea of what that might be like!

To us, pushing has felt a little different with each birth. In the lying down position it can basically feel like you're pushing out the biggest poo you've ever done. It can be tiring (this is why rest, food and water are all recommended during the first stage of labour, to give you enough energy for the second stage). You will also feel lots of pressure down there, like your butt is stretching beyond belief. The great news is that babies' heads are super squishy – they're designed to mould and stretch to make it through the birth canal. It is *not* like pushing a rock-hard bowling ball out, which is a description we've heard before (another lovely fear-inducing story!). You will feel the baby's head descend and then, after the contraction is over, the head will often retract a little. It's like two steps forwards, one step back, until finally the head will stay down as it's crowning. This is true for all positions, although if you've opted for a position that utilises gravity, this stage should be easier to navigate. It is really important to try and *slow* this next bit down, as we'll explain shortly.

To push, take a deep breath and use those lower ab muscles to bear down into your rectum (you can actually practise this while doing your poos on the toilet during pregnancy). Many people will tell you to hold your breath while pushing, but some women who do this end up losing energy and power in the pushing stage. (It also caused Teresa to burst all of her face capillaries in birth numero uno!) Instead, release the breath steadily while maintaining the power of bearing down.

Oh, and if you haven't already figured it out, you're probs gonna poop at this point! All good and NORMAL. Someone will swiftly wipe it away or fish it out of the water with a net (thanks, Mark!).

SPONTANEOUS VS COACHED PUSHING

With spontaneous pushing, the birthing woman follows her urges to push, instinctively bearing down when her body tells her to. In the latent phase of labour (mentioned above), your baby is passively working its way down the birth canal and you won't have the urge to push yet. It's important to preserve your energy during this time. Rest, take sips of water and prepare to work with your body to birth your baby. Active pushing begins the moment mama starts to feel the urge to push. She listens to her body and bears down with the amount of power that her instincts tell her to, being encouraged by a midwife or care provider.

Coached pushing, while considered by many to be the 'old way', is when the birthing mother is told when to push regardless of whether they have the urge to. Often women are lying on their backs with their legs held back by midwives. The birthing woman is told to take a deep breath in and hold it while pushing as hard as possible to the count of ten. Concerns have been raised about the potential adverse effects of this kind of pushing technique on fetal oxygenation and heart rate. Because the perineum is stretched out when a labouring woman is lying on her back, studies suggest that this position can increase the risk of perineal trauma and tearing.

Teresa: I had a home birth transfer with my first delivery. When I got to the hospital I had been in labour for two days and it had stalled when I was 10 centimetres dilated. It was quite an unusual situation, and poor positioning of the baby was to blame. I was given a little Pitocin and was told to lie down on the bed to push. A few nurses came in and pinned my legs back as far as they could go and they instructed me when to push, counting to 10 and telling me to push with 'all my might' and boy did I ever! I focused on pushing as though I was going number 2 – it was really, really challenging work, his head descending then going back in again, descending then going back in again. Had I known about working with gravity I would've insisted on birthing in an upright position.

Maternal-led (i.e. spontaneous) pushing is becoming the preferred way to deliver our babies. However, sometimes during birth things arise that are out of our control, and despite our best intentions our birth preferences will have to shift. It is essential to listen to the guidance of your birthing team. Coached pushing may be necessary and most beneficial during your second stage for a variety of reasons. If you've been administered epidural anaesthesia, sometimes the bearing down sensation will be lessened and coached pushing is required.

BREATHING BABY DOWN

This technique for bringing baby out, usually taught in hypnobirthing classes, is all about utilising your breath and slooooowing it doooown. When your baby is starting to crown and you're feeling the stretch, avoid the tendency to just go for the massive pushes, even if your body is trying to dispel the baby rapidly. Work with the sensations of your body and start to pant – yup, just like a dog after a huge hike, fast in and out breaths (also known as the breath of fire in kundalini yoga). This should slow everything down and allow your vagina to stretch nice and slowly. You can give a few 'little grunts', as Teresa's midwife, Julie, calls them – small and short pushes incorporated in with the panting breaths. The combination of the smaller pushes and this breathing technique can make for a much gentler transition in the crowning stage. In our experience, you can avoid the 'ring of fire', especially if you've opted for a water birth.

This technique may help with avoiding tears. Tensing up the vagina can also cause damage so, as Ina May Gaskin says, think 'loose lips, loose bottom'. Using raspberry lips and relaxing your jaw helps to relax your pelvic floor, too, which is highly beneficial when pushing a baby out.

Many women fear tearing and may even choose not to give birth vaginally because of it. Empowering women to know the capabilities of their bodies, encouraging preparation with perineal massage in the last few weeks leading up to birth, yoga breathing, visualisation and mindfulness preparation can all help a woman build the trust that will enable her to believe she can birth her baby. Fear and denial of the overwhelming sensation to open one's bowels can cause the perineal muscles to tense up, so reassurance can be beneficial when that happens. Most of the research now favours using warm compresses on the perineum (with the woman's consent) once the presenting part is visible, and I also find that using some non-perfumed oil (almond, coconut or olive) over the perineum reduces the tension. Being in water will have a softening effect, too. Positions using gravity, such as standing, all fours and squatting encourage descent with the natural urges to push. Importantly, though, as the head is crowning the midwife or doctor may suggest a position to reduce or relieve the pressure on the perineum. When birth is imminent, verbal guidance to the mum from the midwife with each push can also lessen the incidence of tearing.

—JULIE SCHILLER, CLINICAL MIDWIFE

THINGS WE DIDN'T KNOW: POSTERIOR BIRTH

Teresa: Bodhi was in a posterior position, which means he was facing my abdomen rather than my back. Usually this happens without any preindicative symptoms during the pregnancy. At the time I didn't know much about it, and just accepted that things didn't go textbook, but as above I've since learned that when a baby is posterior it can cause many complications during labour, including the following ones that I experienced.

- My labour was longer (a total of around 30 hours, including both early and active), stronger and less rhythmic than expected, with stop-start contractions.
- From around 6 centimetres dilation I experienced a lot of pain and tension in my back, which is known as back labour.
- Bodhi did not engage, even during the pushing stage.
- My labour stalled, so I had to be given four drops of Pitocin to bring on my contractions again.

I tore a little as Bodhi came out, where his ear caught me as Dr Crane was rotating his head – I was lucky not to have a more serious tear, but breathing and lots of coconut oil seemed to help!

There are other complications that can be prevalent too, which thankfully I personally didn't experience (such as needing to use a vacuum, epidural, caesarean section, etc.). If I had been aware of Bodhi's position beforehand, I would've made an effort to turn him, but we didn't find out until the back labour started, so I rode the experience as it came. Had I known I would've taken all the steps to get him into a more favourable position well before the birth, which I did with my second and third babies as they seemed to be posterior again. It helped a lot (ZERO back labour!), so I'd recommend speaking to your doctor about anything pre-emptive you can do to maximise your chances of having a gentler birth.

Having experienced these complications during Bodhi's birth, I knew I wanted a different experience with Forest. I watched a YouTube video of Ina May talking about preventing tearing in birth, in which she explained how to slow this stage down and allow the body to help you along. She discussed the panting and the loose horse lips, and transitioning between the two breath techniques. I found it absolutely invaluable. Weeks later, when I was in transition in the water birthing tub, I could feel a lot of pressure at the front near my urethra, which is where I tore during my first birth. Julie instructed me to come onto my hands and knees to distribute the pressure and it made all the difference. Immediately I felt light and less tight. I started alternating between the horse lips breathing and the fast panting. Between those two breath styles and telling myself to stretch, I was able to open up really slowly. I gave two little pushes and his head slowly came out, then his body was out in the next push. I was so elated – not only did I not tear, but I didn't feel the burning I had the first time round. I'd managed to slow it all down and let my body, my midwife and the knowledge I'd gained guide me.

Some women experience a very intense burning sensation as the baby's head is crowning. This happens in many births, but fear not, it doesn't happen in all.

If you do experience the ring of fire, no matter what position you're in, unless it's a medical emergency you can *slow it down*. Take back the power and only push when your body tells you to. Resist the urge to 'just get the damn thing out', as this mindset can be the reason some women tear.

Teresa: I remember the ring of fire with Bodhi very well, as it was at this moment that I tore and let out a scream! I was new to all of this pushing and labour stuff and I just pushed when they said push. If I had known that you can slow down this second stage and lessen the intensity of the burn I would've been doing all the tricks to make that happen. I was a new mama and just listened to my instruction, pushing like my life depended on it – and yeeeeouch that fire BURNED. With my subsequent births I didn't go the route of coached pushing. I let my instincts lead the way, and Julie allowed me to listen to my body, and those times I didn't experience the ring of fire.

Sarah: With both of my births my husband was my absolute rock. He had no problem getting in on the dirty side of birth. He held me, wiped fluids off my body, followed me around cleaning things off our floor. My favourite was his coconut oil job: he was in charge of my vagina. He poured an entire bottle of coconut oil on me and Esmé's head as she was slipping into this world, and that 11 pound (5 kg) baby came out smoothly.

NATURAL PAIN RELIEF

There are many options for pain relief during your labour, and while we have both opted for and been able to have births without medication (but most certainly with a medical team), we have many other friends who have had amazingly positive experiences using medicated pain management. We will discuss those options and share our friends' experiences a little later in the chapter, but first, here are some natural techniques that gave us welcome relief.

WATER

Water is particularly helpful during both labour and birth as a warm temperature can help alleviate the intensity of the sensations. Warm water immersion can reduce your stress levels, provide a feeling of weightlessness and enhance your oxytocin levels.[2] Sometimes getting into the water too early might slow contractions down, so it's great to start utilising the bath once established labour has begun.

> **Sarah:** During my labour with Wyatt, the water helped me like nothing else could. I was at 4 centimetres and wasn't progressing, so I was focusing hard on everything I had ever read, trying to remember any 'tricks' I could. What I actually needed was to let go and just be in the moment. My midwife suggested I get in the birthing tub, and for the next four hours Eric held my head, gliding my body from side to side as I slipped deeper and deeper into the other world of labour. I dilated from 4 to 9 centimetres in those four hours. My body and my mind were able to relax and let go. My rushes were about 2 minutes apart still, and in between each rush I would fall into the deepest sleep. It would feel as though I had slept for hours. It was such an awesome surge of energy for me. Eric held a four-hour squat position and took a very heavy load of keeping my head above water. He became the most incredible partner I could ever ask for, and the water allowed me to float and ride the waves in a much more relaxed way.

Teresa: Having a water birth and labouring utilising water as a natural pain reliever was a massive game changer for me. It was like night and day compared to birthing Bodhi on the bed in the hospital, especially when it came to pushing my babies out.

MOVEMENT

It can be really helpful to move your body in all the ways – we're talking shimmying, rolling, spiralling, circling, stomping, swaying . . . This can be cathartic, and can also help baby get into an optimal position for birth. It helps them wriggle into all the space available to them, and also helps to get us in our bodies and out of our heads. It's very easy to get in our own way when we start panicking about the next contraction or wave. Dancing helps move the feeling through the body, and can also distract you from the little committee in your mind that might just be telling you you can't do this. Not only can you do it: you are doing it. The contractions can't be stronger than you, because they *are* you!

Labour is one of the most physical activities a human body can go through, so understanding how your muscles stretch and contract will help you navigate your labour. Not to mention that dancing and swaying your hips in labour can help your baby descend into the birth canal.

– SONYA BISHOP, BIRTH AND POSTPARTUM DOULA

Sarah: I was glad that I'd been walking those 3 to 5 miles every day during my first pregnancy, because when I was 6 centimetres dilated (at around 6 am) my midwife suggested I walk for two hours. ANYTHING my midwife told me to do, I did it. Is it comfortable to walk when you are in labour? Well, it wasn't for me, but it didn't matter: I wanted Wyatt out so I would do anything to make that happen. For the first hour Eric walked with me while my doula rested, and the second hour my doula walked with me while he rested.

Then, when my midwife decided to break my water to help Wyatt start making his way down, he came down a little off, and since he was so big it caused my cervix to swell. For the next few hours, I walked the stairs sideways to try and reposition him. I danced to African drum music, shook my hips in a not-so-graceful way, and did what felt like 1000 squats with the peak of my contractions to get that baby down!

WARM AND COLD COMPRESSES

When preparing your hospital bag, grab some flannels (between six and ten will do), wet them and then drop essential oils of your favourite scents on them. Chuck them in individual zip lock bags and put them in the fridge. Don't forget to bring them to the hospital or birth centre when it's time to go. The cold temperature with the familiar and soothing scent feels both amazing and soothing when pressed onto your face or held against your tummy where the cramping is. Some women prefer a gel heat pack that you can warm up and hold against any area of tension, like your lower tummy or back if you're experiencing back labour.

> **Teresa:** During my labour with Poet, when I was in the shower, my friend Cass brought me sips of water and was handing me the cold scented flannels I had prepared. I used them on my face and they felt amazing. I loved the juxtaposition of the wet flannels and the heat of the water. It really helped.

MASSAGE

Light touch massage is a beautiful way to feel relaxed and release any anxiety or strain you may be experiencing (let's get real: you're birthing a baby, so there's gonna be some of that involved!). Have your partner or doula lightly run their fingertips along your back, shoulder, neck, arms, etc. It feels really loving and nurturing, and if nothing else it's a nice distraction from the baby trying to exit your vag! Some women love a stronger massage, and counterpressure in the hips and lower back can sometimes be a godsend. Just make sure you instruct those around you so they know what you need. Another tip that's random but rad: grab a long sock, put two tennis balls in it and tie it off at the top. This creates a nice little massager that can be worked into your lower back if you're having lower back pressure. It's an inexpensive and simple tool, but is really helpful.

> **Teresa:** I was waiting for my body to shift into the place of being ready to push out little Poet, the rushes roaring closer and stronger. At that moment as I was bracing myself to be ready, Bodhi walked over and did a light touch massage on my shoulders – he'd seen it done in a birthing video we'd watched together. It felt so sweet and loving, and we had a moment together, his hand on top of mine. I told him, 'Your sister is going to be here so soon.'

AFFIRMATIONS

Some of you might be rolling your eyes, thinking the whole 'your thoughts become things' idea is BS, but hang with us a sec – let us tell you how it works! It's all about the (science-backed) mind–body connection and using the power of positive words to help alleviate any fear that arises, which in turn eases perception of pain. This can really influence how you process your response to what you're experiencing. You know how when a little kid falls over, they're fine until they see the blood, and then panic and fear sets in and suddenly they're screaming in pain? That's how powerful our minds are, so keeping our thoughts positive can help manage the pain level and lessen our fixation on it. Here are some helpful affirmations we leaned on during our births.

- Each surge brings me closer to my baby.
- All over the world there are thousands of women birthing with me.

- I trust my body, I trust my baby.

- My body, my baby and I are working as a team.

- The strength of a contraction is the strength of my own body.

- My muscles work in complete harmony to make birthing easier.

- I am surrounded by love.

- I was made to give birth.

- I am opening beautifully.

- Thank you body, thank you baby.

- This will all be over so fucking soon. (Hehe! And it will!)

Sarah: The months leading up to Esmé's birth were challenging, heart-breaking, and a bucket of emotions I am not sure how to begin to describe. Simply yet delicately put, my father died only four months before Esmé was born. In my first month of my last trimester I read a eulogy at his memorial, sang songs in his honour, celebrated his life and said goodbye to a piece of my childhood, my heart, and a comfort I could never replace.

The miracle of this baby inside of me was a light we were all so eager to see. My whole family was anticipating the news of the new baby and in those last few weeks I kept imagining their souls crossing paths, one on the way into this world and one on the way out.

I made the choice at some point in my pregnancy to approach Esmé's birth with joy – after quite a few months of sadness, I really wanted to feel all the good things that were happening inside of me. So I guess you could say I set an intention with the word *joy*. This word was something I thought about a lot: I wanted to accept each 'rush' with love and joy and ask my body to make the rushes bigger and stronger. I wanted to feel elated through the process and I wanted my body to be filled with all kinds of happy feelings. This became a sort of mantra for the birth and it carried me all the way through.

Your voice can be such an amazing tool throughout the birthing process. Finding the vocalising that works for you is all about trial and error: start with a low vibration sound and see how that feels throughout the contraction. Sometimes you'll want to switch it up and move into a sweet, sighing sound before returning back to a deeper, more guttural vibration.

Midwives know that when a labouring woman feels safe, private and undisturbed she will move unrestrictedly and make sounds uninhibitedly. Making sounds during labour helps women to shift their consciousness into a deeper, calmer state of mind. Two of the most effective sounds you can use during labour and birth are:

↘ The 'hummming' sound

Make a low humming sound with your lips closed but jaw relaxed.
The vibration of the lips increases the release of endorphins and other relaxation hormones.

↘ The 'arhhh' sound

Make a long 'arhhh' sound. The sound opens the throat and with you visualising the pelvic bowl opening you become wider and wider as more air is released. Experience the correlation between your relaxed throat and your relaxed bottom.
Remember to drop your chin to allow the sound to travel down and out.

Vocal toning helps you to:

↘ Relax and open the muscle fibres in the pelvic bowl, allowing the pelvic floor to open with more ease and help you birth your baby more quickly.

↘ Create the optimum level of hormones and chemical action in the body for birthing your baby.

You may find that during labour, the low tones will create more opening than the higher tones. A low deep 'arhh' is going to be more effective than a high 'arhh'.

—SUZANNE SWAN, FOUNDER OF YOGABABY AUSTRALIA

Teresa: As mentioned, my second labour, with Forest, went much faster than my first one and I had to be rushed into the hospital by Mark and my friend Kat. On the way there I was in the back of the car hanging over the seats, my head in the boot, swaying my hips and rocking. I remember being at a traffic light and waving to the very shellshocked people who pulled up behind us! I used a low moaning sound to work through it – except when I heard Kat in the passenger seat, telling Mark we were going the wrong way. I lifted one corner of the flannel that was draped over my face and, between rushes, used a different kind of vocalisation: 'AHHH! USE THE GPS!'

VISUALISATION

This is a method of natural pain relief that both of us have used. Through our work and preparation with hypnobirthing we were encouraged to picture a place that felt calm and peaceful to us, somewhere empowering. For Teresa's first birth that place was at the base of the Bodhi tree, with a clear sky and a warm slight breeze; for Forest's birth it was floating over the water in the ocean; and for Poet's birth it was the image of Poet looking into Teresa's eyes. For Sarah, those places were walking a long path on a warm day to the ocean, hearing the sounds of the ocean on the shore, and imagining feeling weightless in the water.

Find what works for you, the images that bring you to a place of calm. Familiarise yourself with your image, even if it's just a colour – it should feel safe, like home. Meditate on it every day in the lead-up to birth so when you're in the middle of your birthing experience it will be easy to access, as it'll be so familiar to you.

Visualisation is a fantastic tool you can use in both your preparation for labour and as a comfort measure during the birth itself. It is simply a technique that enables you to tune inwards and 'drift off' to a nice, comfortable safe place in your mind – a bit like daydreaming with intent. There is a great deal of research that shows the emotional, physical and mental benefits of taking time out to just be, to relax and let your mind wander. For pregnancy and labour it can be one of the most powerful tools to help you stay calm, relaxed, focused and in control of how you are responding to contractions – it is wonderfully beneficial to focus your attention on something specific. By activating different parts of your brain, you are intercepting the nerve impulses from your uterus to your brain, thereby reducing your perception of the intensity of the contractions.

– MAGGIE HOWELL, CLINICAL HYPNOTHERAPIST AND FOUNDER OF NATALHYPNOTHERAPY.CO.UK

Teresa: With my second birth, floating in water in the bathtub helped with the visualisation I was using, which was being in the sunlit ocean and floating over waves. I was imagining Forest and kept picturing his face. I kept repeating to myself, 'Each rush brings me closer to him.'

ASSISTED NON-MEDICAL PAIN RELIEF

There are so many different methods to relieve pain and every woman's body will respond differently. These non-medical methods work for some but others don't respond well or can have a reaction, so make sure to discuss your options with your care provider.

TENS MACHINE

The TENS machine is considered a natural labour tool and its praises have been sung by women around the world for many years. Both portable and non-invasive, it's a handheld machine that sends electric currents into four sticky pads that you place on your lower back. You control the intensity of the impulses. It works by blocking the pain messages that are sent to your brain. It can't be used if you're labouring in water (obvs), but it's nice to hire and have handy just in case. Some people may experience a buzzing, tingling or prickly sensation while in use and others may find it feels uncomfortable.

WATER THERAPY

This is a pain relief option that involves sterile water being injected into your lower back, predominantly to assist with back pain in labour. Researchers believe it works by altering the way your body perceives pain, but there isn't sufficient evidence yet to show that this technique reduces the need for other pain relief. The injections are done during contractions and can cause a stinging sensation similar to a bee sting. If this method works, it has been known to help relieve pain for up to two hours. Chat with your doctor and/or midwife about whether they offer this option, as it's less commonly used for relieving pain during labour.

ASSISTED MEDICAL PAIN RELIEF

EPIDURAL

An epidural is an injection of local anaesthetic administered into your lower back, which provides effective pain relief by prohibiting feeling to a certain part of your body. It is localised, so it doesn't affect feeling throughout your whole body; only the nerve signals communicating with your belly, back and cervix are numbed. This is the most popular method of pain relief administered to women in labour – approximately one third of labouring women in Australia opt for an epidural. Walking epidurals are increasing in popularity, as they give you more freedom to move around during labour and birth. Walking epidurals use the same medications as a classic epidural, but the smaller doses administered mean you experience greater sensations during contractions, while they still take the edge off.

There are a number of varying options when it comes to getting an epidural. Most women say that, while it can be uncomfortable to try and remain still as the epidural is administered, the injection itself feels similar to a bee sting. With sweet relief soon to follow, it's become a popular birthing aid for many women. Is there an 'Oops I missed the boat' point? Technically, it's only too late when the baby is crowning. However, if delivery looks likely to happen within the hour, many doctors may say it's too late to have an epidural. Speak to your doctor about your pain relief options.

Epidurals have their place but fully informed consent is needed, with disclosure of what this invasive procedure involves and its risks (including hypotension, the need for continuous fetal monitoring, an IVT and a urinary catheter, and – if it's not a 'walking epidural' – limitations on mobility). The decrease in the sensation to bear down in the second stage that results from an epidural can necessitate more coached pushing in restricted positions. Interestingly, when the epidural has finally been administered, it is not uncommon for labouring mothers to find they have developed a strong urge to push and it possibly wasn't needed anyway.

– JULIE SCHILLER, CLINICAL MIDWIFE

Megan Gale's story: the positives of an epidural

When I was pregnant with my son, River, I wanted to try my best to have a natural birth but was also happy and prepared to have an epidural if need be. That said, I was far more stubborn about it than I thought I'd be.

I had what's known as an in-coordinate labour (meaning contractions are basically all over the shop). My doctor broke my waters to get labour under way and the intensity increased tenfold, so I jumped on the gas to ease the pain – but I took on too much, which made me feel sick to my stomach rather than lucid and energised for when I came to push. Feeling far from ready to push, I had to reassess: my main goal was to be able to push my baby out, and I knew I was being stubborn and enduring the pain for no good reason. A little voice inside said, 'For God's sake, have the epi!'

Once I made the call, I wanted that needle in my back immediately – but it didn't happen quite how I thought it would. It took 45 minutes for the anaesthetist to arrive (which felt like a lifetime) and he then had to verbally walk me through the process. There was paperwork to sign, then he had to prep himself, prep me – and then it came time to have the needle.

The epidural kicked in about 20 minutes later and it was blissful. I could still feel my contractions (like mild period cramps) so I wasn't totally numb, but I could finally start to relax! After 20 more minutes, I was sitting up, sipping peppermint tea and chatting with my partner, Shaun, while we waited patiently for our baby. When the time came to push, I was able to be present and focused on what I was doing, and actually felt amazing. The epidural meant I could rest and regenerate enough to achieve my goal.

The morals to this story? Be flexible and don't beat yourself up if the birth veers away from what you had hoped. Don't assume that once you request an epidural, someone will rush in and ease your pain immediately.

And lastly, don't feel guilty for having one. At the end of the day, you want this to be a memorable experience and the most important thing is for you and your baby to come through it all, healthy, safe and happy.

This is nitrous oxide, and is a great option for those who are looking for pain relief but don't want an epidural. You're able to monitor how much you take in, as you are in control of bringing the mask up to your face and sucking that glorious gas in! It makes you feel high, and dulls the pain but doesn't take it away entirely, unlike an epidural. Teresa's mum tells us that she took it at the peak of her contractions and it was very helpful to counteract the pain (Teresa was a fat baby!). Plus it made her feel euphoric – nice. There can be side effects to nitrous oxide, however: some women have reported having bad reactions and have said it made them feel detached, sleepy and nauseous.

A NOTE FROM THE DADS

Mark: I'll just talk about our most recent birth, Poet's, which was like a divine, mystical experience. We all became transfixed by the rhythmic waves of energy Teresa was experiencing during each surge, watching her increasingly process it – it seemed like she was in ecstasy. It was extremely hypnotic. I felt like I was sitting outside my body as I watched the room holding the group of women and my wife in the centre of it, our children there watching on. It was deeply, deeply profound. I could see how Teresa had learnt from her past birth experiences, how she'd built off the combined efforts of each previous birth. As a birthing partner I knew my role was to be a support system. I had deep trust in her and this process and I think that's my role: to be a steady, gentle reassurance and literally hold her up – in every sense – in the moments when she needed to be held.

Eric: Watching Sarah give birth was the single most transformational event of my adult life. Her courage and commitment to her birthing plan, her physical ability and grace, her presence and passion, and her inextinguishable strength forever altered my view of her, our relationship, and ultimately motherhood. In a flash of blood and tears I was connected to Sarah and the journey of the generations of mothers that came before her. She is a goddess, a warrior and a f*cking gangster. I love her more fearlessly and deeply because of it. As partners we do whatever is necessary and are present, loving, supportive and compassionate. I actively invested myself in the process and jumped in the trench with her – but I definitely had the easy job!

THE THIRD STAGE OF LABOUR

Post pushing, when your baby has made their way earth side, your body will be running on some sort of hormone/adrenaline-filled cocktail. At this moment you may feel like you want to rest and have everyone leave the room so you can cuddle and coo with your new little love, but what we didn't realise our first times around is that our work was not quite over. Your uterus will be contracting as your baby starts to find their way to your breast and your body will still need to birth the placenta.

Teresa: An hour after Bodhi's delivery my placenta still hadn't come down (this is what's known as a retained placenta) and my body wouldn't contract any more, so it was decided that I would have to have a manual extraction. Dr Crane explained that most patients he had done this on had had an epidural or other pain relief methods, which I hadn't. In the same breath, he told me he could do it in under one minute. Given that I had come this far, wanted to be able to be discharged that night and was feeling good, we decided to go ahead and do it without pain relief. I won't go into details, but let's just say there were some never-said-before expletives thrown around! I have never experienced such blackout pain as that, but he did it so quickly and efficiently, and soon enough my babe was back in my arms for me to stare at adoringly.

CAESAREAN BIRTHS

This is a big shout-out to the caesarean mamas out there! You are bad-ass mother birthers and this section is for you.

You may have a planned caesarean because that's how you feel most comfortable birthing, you may have medical reasons for needing a caesarean, or perhaps a C-section is in your future because your intended vaginal birth may turn out differently than you expect. Either way, it's great to be informed about your rights and choices. Two great resources that provide more information on caesareans are ranzcog.edu.au and betterhealth.vic.gov.au (click through to the pages on this topic).

WHAT A CAESAREAN INVOLVES

Raisingchildren.net.au provides lots of useful information about caesarean births.

Before your surgery you'll be prepared for an anaesthetic. A spinal anaesthetic is normally used for a planned caesarean birth while an epidural is more likely to be used for an unplanned or emergency caesarean birth. You'll only have a general anaesthetic if the other options are not possible for you, or your baby needs to be born very quickly.

A needle will be inserted in the back of your hand or your elbow so that you can have a drip. In the operating theatre, your abdominal area will be cleaned with antiseptic and covered with sterile cloths to reduce the chance of infection. You'll have a catheter inserted to keep your bladder empty.

If you have a spinal anaesthetic or epidural you will be awake and able to breathe normally. You may feel tugging and pulling sensations but you will not feel pain.

Remember to check with the hospital staff whether it's okay to take photos or video of your baby being born. In particular, you'll need permission to take photos of any of the hospital staff or equipment.

GENTLE CAESAREAN

Caesarean sections are one of the most common surgeries performed in a hospital. In 2018, 33 per cent of all births in Australia were by caesarean section.[3] There is a real movement towards making these operations a more pleasant and less sterile experience for parents, and a new way of doing things, known as a 'gentle', 'family-centred' or 'natural' caesarean, is proving to be an empowering experience for mamas and papas. The improvements are designed to help promote the immediate connection between mother and baby. The gentle caesarean practice includes:

- clear drapery for mama to be able to see baby being lifted out
- IV and monitoring equipment placed on sides of chest and/or arms so that

baby can be placed immediately on mama's chest

- only one of mama's arms is strapped down, to allow for nursing and cuddling baby once born, and baby stays on mama for the remainder of the surgery
- music is allowed to be played in the room
- a photographer or videographer is permitted to be in the room documenting the birth.

EMERGENCY CAESAREAN

Emergency caesareans can be necessary in a number of births, and are just another reminder of the importance of staying open-minded during your birthing experience. At the end of the day, the most important thing is ensuring that both you and your baby are healthy. Situations can arise where it is decided that a fast C-section delivery is the safest option for everyone involved. It may be a shock, it may throw you for a loop, or you may not even have time to process it, but don't worry, there will be time for that later. If this happens to you, focus on the fact that your baby is about to be born. Take some deep breaths, practise the visualisations you've been working on and know that this decision is being made for the good of everyone.

Karine's story: Quincy's birth by emergency caesarean

I thought my waters had broken in bed at 1am and excitedly woke my husband, but when I went to the bathroom and found blood in my pyjama pants, I couldn't believe my eyes. I instantly knew something was wrong and went into a panic, yelling at my husband to call the hospital.

Our arrival there was a blur as our doctor explained that she thought I'd experienced a placental abruption, where the placenta detaches from the wall of the uterus. Of course, my mind went to worst case scenario. The doctor recommended an emergency C-section and minutes later I was wheeled into theatre, accompanied by three extra on-call doctors and theatre nurses – the level of care was fantastic.

The relief when I heard that newborn cry was immense. I just couldn't stop crying! It wasn't long until I had Quincy skin-to-skin on my chest and there she stayed while I was stitched and spent time in recovery. I was so thankful for that time – no one bothered us, allowing us to bond with our beautiful daughter.

I'd been really hoping to have an intervention-free birth and had spent a lot of time on my vaginal birth plan. I'd listened to hypnobirthing podcasts and read up on natural ways to manage pain and, to be honest, the thought of a caesarean had not once crossed my mind. But the fact that I did have one in the end has not fazed me in the slightest. Ultimately, both me and my baby girl are healthy and thriving after that awful initial scare and that's all that is important to me. I honestly look at the caesarean now as a positive experience.

IF YOUR BIRTH DIDN'T GO AS PLANNED

Once your baby is in your arms and the panic of it all has calmed down, you may be left feeling a little shellshocked at any sudden or unexpected change in plans for your birth. This is normal, and to be expected. It's important to allow yourself to feel the feelings, whether that is mourning the vaginal birth you had envisioned or just coming to terms with your recovery period. Around day three, when your milk comes in (give or take a few days) you will experience a hormonal drop. Sometimes if you've experienced a birth that was different from your ideal, you may find yourself transferring some of the emotions that can come with that hormonal dip onto your birthing experience. In these times it's imperative to talk about what you're going through. Choose a friend, your partner or your care provider to share your experiences with. Another amazing resource is the Pregnancy, Birth and Baby Helpline, through which you can reach a maternal child health nurse, on 1800 882 436. We'll talk more about the mental recovery from birth in Chapter 6.

THINGS WE DIDN'T KNOW: CONTROL IS AN ILLUSION

Teresa: My birthing journey with Bodhi was such a life-changing event for me, not just because it made me a mother, which had always been my greatest dream, but also because it taught me the gift in surrendering. I've always been an I-prefer-to-be-in-control kind of person, but to have experienced unforeseen complications with Bodhi's arrival into the world gave me such a pearl of wisdom: things will unravel in life in unexpected ways, and however hard we try to have situations meet our expectations, really, we aren't in control. The only thing we have the power to control is our openness to what our experience becomes, even if it's totally different from what we envisioned. I know now that Bodhi's birth was exactly the birth we were supposed to have and it was even more impactful on me than I had imagined. I loved it. Through all the challenges and unforeseen hurdles, being able to ride the experience with a sense of surrender, presence and acceptance has been the single greatest lesson I've learnt in my life, and it so beautifully set me up for the adventures in parenting.

ZEN NOTES

- Do your research, learn your techniques, write tips in your journal. Read, watch, listen.

- Ina May Gaskin. Nuff said.

- Visualise your dream birth, write about it, talk to your baby about it and then Let. It. Go.

- Stay open, present and aware of your options. Ensure your hubby/wife/ lover/birth partner can advocate for your choices if you cannot.

- Movement, visualisation, water, affirmations, vocalisation and a variety of positions are all invaluable tools if an unmedicated birth is what you desire.

- Walking epidurals are awesome if you go down the pain meds route, giving you more freedom to move about.

- If available to you, birthing positions that utilise gravity are awesome and help prevent tears, making that second stage easier. And who doesn't want that?

- Lastly, you're an amazing warrior woman, a bad-ass birther and no matter how your baby comes into this world, you are incredible, brave and a wondrous creature to be admired and celebrated. A golden statue should be erected in your honour!

YOUR BODY

FIVE

You've done it! You've worked your way through pregnancy, spent all those months caressing your belly, preparing your home, folding tiny clothes, navigating the sleepless nights and dreams about birthing puppies (Sarah), and you've birthed a baby (not a dog), or you've adopted one (again, a baby, not a dog – this is *not* the time for a new puppy). And now this blissful (albeit needy) little baby is finally here, you just need to figure out what the heck you're doing. Welcome to parenthood! Gulp.

You've heard the horror stories: 'You'll never sleep again!', 'The newborn days are the worst', 'Your life ends with a baby!' But we're here to tell you that, while you might have *some* of those feelings *some* of the time, raising children is a whirlwind of many colourful adventures, both great and not-so-great. There are going to be really hard times but there are also going to be days when your heart feels so full you think it might burst, you're so moved just watching your children being in the world. Ask a parent in the later stages of their life about their happiest memories and we bet they'll say one of them was raising their children.

So with pregnancy and labour done and dusted, let's step into your new life as a mama, complete with your snuggly new baby.

THE FOURTH TRIMESTER

This precious time from when baby takes their first breath earth side until they're 12 weeks old is known as the 'fourth trimester'. It's helpful to think of the first three months of your baby's life as the final trimester because it is such a transitional phase: one that brings many new changes for mama and baby as you adapt to life together. These initial weeks are an adjustment period as you get to know your little one while also recovering from birth. The end of this fourth trimester is often bittersweet: on the downside, it signifies the end of the newborn phase, but on the upside, *it signifies the end of the newborn phase!* Can we get a hell yeah!?

These next three chapters are going to look at some of the things that crop up during the first 12 weeks of life with a newborn, in particular the peaks and valleys that we've encountered during the fourth trimester with our own kids. We've broken it up into Body, Mind and Baby, as the fourth trimester impacts all three. This is a period that's not often spoken about, so we want to provide you with as much information as we can to ensure you feel well equipped and aware of everything that is going on. Remember, you are not alone in any of these experiences. We're kicking off with your body because, Mama, you've just given the gift of life, and with that comes a few obvious and not so obvious things you need to know.

YOUR BODY

Your body will be going through all sorts of changes postpartum and it's pretty wild to see how it recovers from birth! As you know by now, pregnancy is tailored individually to every mama, and it's the same with postpartum changes. Comparing yourself to filtered 'postpartum bikini bods' on Instagram, or to your best friend/ sister/colleague/neighbour is not going to serve you – it will only bring you down. Your path is your own, and changes will happen as your body allows. Many surprises await, and there's no rhyme or reason as to how long it will take for your body to return to its pre-baby form. All you can do is go easy on yourself, go slow and love your amazing body and its changes. After all, it's just given you the greatest gift imaginable.

> **Teresa:** When I look down at my tummy these days, I see what was once a cool idea at 16 to get my belly button pierced and instantly have buyer's remorse as what stares back at me is a wrinkled, shrivelled-up, floppy belly button with an identity crisis: am I an inny or an outy? (It's both!) At first, I was self-conscious about it but now I've learnt to love my warped belly button and the three babies that it represents. It's my warrior stamp. Now one of my favourite things is to notice other women with similar wrinkly belly buttons and imagine what their swollen bellies once looked like carrying their own babes. Understanding that our bodies have walked a tremendous path allows us to be gentle in our judgements of it, turning negative feelings into gratitude: 'I'm so thankful and proud of my body's capabilities.'

STRAIGHT AFTER YOUR VAGINAL BIRTH

Once your placenta has been delivered, the cord has been cut and you're officially the one keeping your baby alive, you'll experience all sorts of overwhelming emotions. You'll undergo some necessary post-birth checks by your midwife (which, let's be honest, you may not even notice – you'll be distracted by this little miracle you have created). They'll check post-birth bleeding levels and ensure everything is as it should be. If you've had a straightforward vaginal birth you'll most likely be enjoying snuggle time with the floppy ray of sunshine that is your child. If you have had some perineal trauma, your midwife or doctor will need to stitch you up. They will use a local anaesthetic (a numbing injection) to stitch up your tear with dissolvable stitches.

You'll most likely want to stay cuddled up with your baby, resting and using as little energy as possible. You've just triumphed in life's great marathon so you'll feel pretty exhausted! Luckily, endorphins will be pulsating through you so you might be feeling pretty high – some women describe the first hours after birth as an out-of-body experience. This isn't always the case, however – some women report feeling depressed, numb, and experiencing a sense of anticlimax. All feelings are valid, completely normal and shared by many.

Teresa: With my first birth I felt completely shell-shocked immediately afterwards. I just couldn't believe I had actually gotten through it, and also the physicality of that experience meant I was very depleted. I remember just sitting in a place of processing all the ways in which my birth had turned out differently than I had expected. I was utterly in love with this little baby in my arms; it was a completely out of body experience. I was finally a mother, but whoa, what a crazy two days it had been. With my next two births my elation was through the roof – I kept laughing and crying and telling people I had never been so happy: I was the literal definition of blissed out.

Sarah: With my first birth I had been in labour so long (18 hours) and pushed for four hours, so the time after birth was a haze of exhaustion, bliss, a bit of pain – and I'd be lying if I didn't tell you I had double vision. I fall into the 'out of body' experience category because my hormones and adrenaline kept me going and floated me through the first nursing session, my sweet newborn cuddles and straight into the moment when I said 'my eyes are closing and I can't stop them'. A little bit of sleep brought me back into my body.

Sometimes you can get the post-birth shakes, which is usually from adrenaline, fatigue and the sudden drop in hormones, namely oestrogen. You'll be wrapped up warmly and your care providers will be monitoring you to ensure that you feel comfortable and that all is going well.

Your tummy will probably resemble a withered balloon, all squishy and floppy, and you'll most likely still look pregnant despite having ejected a few kilos of baby. You might feel the need to hold your tummy in while you shuffle over to the bathroom for your first post-birth pee or to shower. Don't worry, it'll go back down at some point – you won't look preggo forever! You can ask for a Tubigrip bandage from your doctor, nurse or midwife to wrap around your belly – it'll help hold it all in and make you feel more supported. Otherwise there are some great postpartum belly wrap options you can buy in advance and bring to your birthing facility – we like wearing the Belly Bandit belly wraps and SRC Health's recovery shorts for several weeks after giving birth, as they can help reduce discomfort. But a good ol' pair of Spanx will also do the trick.

Sarah: I was curious how I would look after having my baby. When I had my first child, I hadn't actually ever seen someone moments after giving birth, but I'd heard you could look six months pregnant still, and that is exactly what I looked like. It felt different to me though. As I snuggled up with my new baby, I loved that my little one had this soft pillow to lie on. I loved my baby lying across my tummy on top of this familiar spot that he grew in for nine months. After having two kids now, my tummy looks different. When I feel a bit off or insecure about the way my skin crepes from stretching, I try to remind myself that this belly stretched to hold giant babies, it was the place they slept and ate for years, and that this tummy needs no criticism – only gratitude.

Your partner and birth support team can help support your body with pillows as you bond with your new baby and focus on baby's first breastfeeding latch (more on this in Chapter 7). This is a beautiful opportunity to have skin-on-skin contact with your baby, so take your top off and lay your naked newborn on your chest. It's always lovely to have your partner do skin-on-skin with babe too; this helps to initiate their own special bond. The benefits of skin-on-skin are wonderful for your baby. It helps release happy hormones (in both parties!), relieves stress, and regulates baby's heartbeat and breathing. By passing baby over for a cuddle with a loved one, you can have a nice warm shower or take a well-earned nap. And trust us, Mama, take the sleep when you can! From both a medical and emotional standpoint, right now sleep is worth its weight in gold. A tip we got from an amazing postpartum doula is to sleep when your baby sleeps. You've just experienced a test of endurance, and even though the adrenaline and endorphins are telling you otherwise, your mind and body need time to rest and recover. Sleep enables your body to do its thang and kickstarts the recovery process, but it's also vital in helping you regulate hormones and rebalance your emotions.

If you've had an epidural, your catheter will be removed about an hour or two post-birth. The amount of numbness experienced by the birthing mother varies, but most women are usually able to begin moving only a couple of hours post-birth. Your body might feel quite stiff after remaining in one place for a prolonged period of time, so if you're feeling able, a walk along the hospital corridor may help to loosen your muscles.

GOING HOME

Depending on your individual birth, you can expect to be discharged anywhere from a few hours to a week post-birth. We know you may be itching to get home, but remember that if your midwife or healthcare professional is keeping you in hospital, it is for a reason. This is the perfect time to rest, relax and soak up all the help, information and advice you can from the team of experts around you. Maybe just have Uber Eats or friends who can cook at the ready if you're as averse to hospital food as we are!

You may be desperate to wear anything that's *not* the maternity clothes you've been wearing for the last nine months. However, bear in mind you will need comfort and, if you are breastfeeding, accessibility. Loose dresses, yoga pants, sweats, V-necks, shirts with buttons and loose flowy cotton clothing will allow you the space you need to heal comfortably and will provide fast and easy access to your breasts.

> **Sarah:** I wore my pregnancy pants for a long time after having my babies. It felt comfortable to me, and I could pull the waistband over my Belly Bandit to help hold everything in place. I loved wearing flowy dresses and loose clothing because I did spend a lot of the time in bed with my babies, nursing and trying to sleep when they were sleeping. Hatch is one of my favourite pregnancy and postpartum brands, and their whole message is that their clothes can be worn both during and after pregnancy. My tip for mamas is to buy yourself a new pair of cosy pyjamas and save them for postpartum!

It's totally normal to experience a lot of bleeding post-birth. This post-birth vaginal discharge is known as lochia. Lochia is made up of blood, mucus, vernix, placental tissue and bacteria, and its release can last between two and six weeks – every body and birth is different. The volume tends to be similar to a heavy period initially, and can include clots, though if there are any clots bigger than a 20-cent piece, or if you are soaking more than one pad per hour, you should contact your care provider. Use maternity pads – these are thicker, longer and more absorbent than your typical period 'super' pad. This is a key pre-birth preparation purchase to pack in your hospital bag! For the next six weeks you and your fanciest granny knickers are going to be besties. Don't worry, you're not gonna want to get frisky during this period anyway.

Sarah: When I was pregnant with my first baby, someone told me to buy myself five pairs of black underwear, really soft, cosy, comfortable ones that I wouldn't have to worry about ruining. I wish I'd taken that advice, because Teresa and my friend Kacy dug through my undie drawer trying to find anything remotely large enough to hold those giant postpartum pads and had no luck! Kacy came to my house the next day with a bunch of black undies and they were my saving grace.

AFTERBIRTH PAINS

As your uterus shrinks back to its pre-pregnancy size you may experience some contraction-like sensations. For most first-time mums these cramps are pretty mild, but the cramps for subsequent pregnancies can be more intense. This might feel similar to being mid-labour again, and typically feels strongest two to four days post-birth. The cramps come on sporadically, but are often triggered by nursing your newborn. You can try the natural pain relief methods discussed in Chapter 4 to help ease the discomfort, or ask your doctor or midwife for recommended pain relief options if what you're experiencing is too uncomfortable.

YOUR LADY BITS

Your vagina will be pretty tender post-birth, and depending on how your pushing stage went – whether you tore, how hard you were pushing, baby's positioning and size, etc. – your recovery will vary. Your midwife or healthcare professional will examine your vagina after birth to ensure everything is healing properly, but even if there was no tearing, you can still expect to be a little tender. There are lots of things you can do to help your nether regions along their healing journey!

Many hospitals give out a peri bottle post-birth. This is a plastic bottle with a squirty lid that you fill with water and use to clean yourself. It is particularly useful for mamas who had stitches, as the water dilutes the pee and makes you feel more comfortable using the bathroom.

A sitz bath is a shallow, warm bath that you sit in, designed to aid in the healing of your perineum. You can DIY at home in your own bathtub, or you can purchase a kit. It soothes soreness, relaxes the perineal muscles and increases blood flow to the area to help reduce swelling. There are so many amazing herbs out there that can assist with soothing sore parts – we like to use lavender oil and witch hazel, as well as any sea salt.

When using a sitz bath, there are a few important things to keep in mind:

- Use cool or warm water, but not hot – your poor perineum will thank you for that!
- Make sure the sitz bath or bathtub is cleaned and disinfected first.
- Ask your health practitioner for guidance on how long to soak for.
- Be gentle when drying afterwards, either patting softly or just air-drying. No rubbing!

Both mum and baby can soak to speed up healing of the umbilical cord and perineum, and you can also fill your peri bottle with your herbal water for use after going to the bathroom.

PERINEAL SPRAY

If you opt out of a sitz bath you can get the same benefits by purchasing a perineal spray. Cooling and filled with natural healing herbs, the spray will help relieve any pains you're experiencing down below. You can order these sprays online (the BodyWise BirthWise Store make a great one, and Earth Mama is always amazing and organic!), or make one yourself using geranium and lavender – be sure to dilute them with water and store in a sterilised bottle.

REFRIGERATED PADS SOAKED IN TEA TREE OR WITCH HAZEL

These will help alleviate any burning you experience down there. The cool temperature is soothing on your vagina and helps with the swelling – plus, they tuck perfectly into your oversized granny undies! (If you experience any redness or itching, see your doctor.)

GEL PADS

Gel pads are little plastic freezer packs filled with gel, and while they're not absorbent and won't soak up any discharge, you can pop them in your pants for sweet relief. They can help with swelling and reducing tenderness.

YOGA BALL

If you're feeling any post-birth pressure down there, you can create counter-pressure by sitting on a yoga ball.

Teresa: My recovery from Bodhi's delivery was much longer than from my subsequent births because of the tear that happened while I was busy pushing like my life depended on it. For two weeks afterwards I had to pee sitting in a bucket of warm water as it was too painful otherwise. Because of how hard I'd pushed, my bottom felt so bruised that I needed help being lifted off and on the couch!

RECOVERY FROM A CAESAREAN BIRTH

Recovering from a caesarean birth will be a longer process, and you need to take it easy. Remember that a caesarean is considered major surgery, and your recovery will be a marathon, not a sprint. It's important to listen to your body and take it s-l-o-w.

Once you are home from the hospital (typically three to four days after a caesarean birth), follow these tips for a faster recovery:

- Don't do any heavy lifting. A good guide is that anything heavier than your baby is a no-go. Ensure your partner or other helpers lift any older siblings.
- Rest when your baby rests. The dishes and laundry can wait (or better yet, get someone else to do them!). REST is most important.
- Keep baby supplies nearby so you don't have to walk a long way.
- Keep snacks next to your bed so you can eat in the middle of the night if you are hungry from breastfeeding.
- Stay very well hydrated.
- Keep the incision site clean. No scrubbing: use soap and water in a gentle wiping manner.
- Use an abdominal wrap. It'll help keep your stitches in place and provides extra muscular support, meaning you can move more comfortably.
- Hold your incision site with a blanket or pillow when laughing, coughing or sneezing.

- Keep a close eye out for any infection warning signs, such as redness, swelling and odour.
- Keep a maxi pad over the top of your C-section scar to help with absorption.
- Use lavender oil and other calming oils in a diffuser to help with natural pain relief.
- Use aloe vera gel or cream on your scar once the wound has closed over. Earth Mama makes a C-section balm that's amazing for any scar.

YOUR PLACENTA

The placenta is often considered the Tree of Life, as it has been the vital lifeline between you and bub, supporting and nourishing baby as it grows throughout pregnancy. Many mamas feel that the placenta is too significant to simply discard after birth. There are a number of options for what you do with your placenta. Here are some of them to consider if you're unsure.

PLANT IT

Teresa: We buried Forest's placenta in our garden and planted 'The Forest Tree' on top of it. It was our way of symbolising our son's connection to the earth. That, and I just couldn't stomach eating it!

MAKE ART OUT OF IT

Enlist someone to take the placenta and make a canvas print of it (there are reputable people who offer this service online). It's a beautiful way to remember the time your placenta nourished your darling, and many people find it more palatable than eating it!

NOTE: If you're considering consuming your placenta we suggest doing your research thoroughly as each woman reacts differently. Many women anecdotally report feeling health benefits, but there is no conclusive evidence to support these claims, and the risks of eating placenta include infection for the mother (and baby if breastfeeding).

You'll need to use a *hell* of a lot of sugar to combat the meaty taste! Honey honey honey, agave, berries, cacao, cinnamon, fruit – whatever you can get your hands on. Put more of those ingredients in than the placenta and it shouldn't taste too bad.

Sarah: My placenta smoothie the first time around was pretty terrible. I was very out of it after my home birth delivery so I drank it even though it didn't taste very good (Eric was delirious on no sleep for several days and made me my kale smoothie with the placenta instead of a yummy fruit smoothie). For my second baby I read the book *The First Forty Days*, and I had my postpartum doula make the placenta smoothie in the book with cacao. It tasted AMAZING.

TURN IT INTO CAPSULES/TINCTURE

There are a number of companies that will collect your placenta and prepare it in a way that enables you to ingest it in capsule form. Although no studies have been done on consuming placenta in a capsule form, some midwives, doulas, care providers and mothers swear by its benefits in fighting off postpartum depression, restoring much-needed nutrients to the mother and helping to boost milk supply.

Sarah: With both babies I made a placenta smoothie and took capsules for weeks after they were born. I'd waited a beat on taking them postpartum with Esmé, but I started feeling some blues because of losing my father so I began to take them religiously.

> **Teresa:** I bought a package to have my placenta from Poet's pregnancy encapsulated and I didn't realise that as a part of the package I would receive placenta body balm. I tentatively opened the tin, smelt it (it smelt wonderful, as it was mixed with essential oils), and then applied it to my face every day for the first two weeks. I had friends say that I've never looked more youthful, haha! Maybe it was the balm or maybe it was the post-baby high I was experiencing. Either way, it was quite a lovely product and from what I could tell it only had a nominal amount of placenta in it.

GET RID OF IT — BUT PHOTOGRAPH IT FIRST!

Okay, so some of us think placentas are kinda gross and wouldn't dream of taking ours home with us. That's fine, you can leave it at the hospital and they will dispose of it. Don't forget to take a photograph of it, though – it's so wild looking, and it's utterly incredible to think that all those twists and turns, colours and nooks were sustaining your baby throughout their time in your uterus. What a marvellous thing!

OTHER BODILY JOYS YOU CAN EXPECT

FATIGUE

Just to state the obvious: birth is hardcore! It's an absolutely amazing achievement and your body really goes through the ringer. Some women will have really complicated recovery periods, while others will travel more smoothly, but either way, your body will need time to heal. Sleep will be interrupted, which will become your new normal – when your baby sleeps, it's important to take the time to nap too. The household duties can wait! Try to bank up as much sleep as you can in these early days. Be gentle with yourself as you ease back into day-to-day routine – you've just grown and birthed a mini-human! Give your body time to recover before you return to the demands of pre-birth life.

NIGHT SWEATS

This is something we were never told about . . . You've just had a baby, the baby is finally asleep and now you've woken up in the middle of the night dripping with sweat – and we mean *dripping*! Night sweats occur because of the rapid drop in oestrogen. During pregnancy your body accumulates 50 per cent more blood and fluid. You no longer need that much fluid, so your body expels it in the form of sweating. The good news? Usually the night sweats are done with by week three postpartum. If your night sweats continue, check in with your care provider and let them know.

BOWEL ISSUES

CONSTIPATION

Some women experience constipation post-birth – dehydration, hormonal drops, caesarean surgery and pain relievers can all lead to issues with pooping! Try eating prunes, upping your fluid intake, having some fresh juices and taking a stroll to get things moving and pay your healthcare provider a visit to see if they can provide additional help.

> **Sarah:** I'd heard a lot of people talk about how scary the first poo postpartum would be. I was a little nervous about this happening, but with my homebirth, my midwife made me feel at ease and helped me by giving me foods to eat that would make this easier. When I birthed in a hospital, I was given a couple of pills to take after I had my baby. I thought they were ibuprofen or something to help ease the swelling, but I was so out of it and tired I took them before even asking what I

had taken. It turns out they had given me stool softeners, which I found out pretty quickly when I started getting stomach cramps and had to dash to the bathroom a few times. I'm sharing this with you because I wish I hadn't taken those pills, so learn from my mishap: if someone at the hospital or birth centre gives you pills to take, ask what they are first so you aren't surprised an hour later!

INCONTINENCE

It's all about the pelvic floor, ladies. Don't go jumping on a trampoline or sneezing without a pad on, because your pelvic floor needs some training! In fact, we recommend taking spare pads and knickers when you're out and about – we've both been caught short by this little postpartum joy! Labour strains the pelvic floor, which needs to learn how to do its job optimally again. Kegel exercises are the key: squeeze the same muscle you would to stop yourself from peeing, hold it for 4 seconds, then release to the count of four. Try to do this 15 times per day for as long as you need to before you feel the tone returning to 'normal'. Let's be honest, pre or post baby, it's always a good idea to strengthen those Kegel muscles!

BREAST ENGORGEMENT

Between days 2 and 5 your breastmilk will come in. Your breasts will feel HUGE, swollen and leaky as that liquid gold fills up your breasts, ready for your little suckling. Sometimes if you produce more milk than your baby drinks you can become engorged and your breasts will feel too full, hot and throbbing.

Sarah: I was not prepared for this. I was told my boobs would get bigger but I didn't understand how hard they would get and how much they would hurt as the milk came in. My midwife noticed how quickly my milk arrived and taught me something that would save me for all my years of breastfeeding. When your boobs feel full and if you feel any hard spots, that could mean you're getting a clogged duct. The best thing to do is deep-tissue breast massage in the shower. Start on the outside of the breast, from your armpit, and use your thumb to press deep into the tissue all the way to the nipple. Do this all around your breast or where you have hard spots until you feel relief. This prevented me from getting mastitis, which is an inflammation of breast tissue sometimes caused by infection or a clogged milk duct. You can also do this massage while baby is nursing, as long as your baby's latch is good and it doesn't disrupt your nursing.

So what do you do when you get engorged? Here are some tips used by permission of La Leche League International, for some of the things you can do to help with engorgement:

- Keep your baby with you – on your chest, in your arms, at your side. Body contact can actually help, and it makes frequent nursing more likely.
- Nurse or express your milk at least every two hours, and at least twice during the night. The more milk that collects in your breasts, the stuffier they get and the harder it is for fluids to move. By taking milk out often, you make it easier for all the fluids in your breast – not just the milk – to move around.
- Move your breasts around gently and massage them in any way that feels good. It may help shift excess fluids.
- Lie back, which keeps your breasts higher than usual. Fluids follow gravity.
- A bag of frozen vegetables can be a cold compress. Wrap it in a towel and put it on your breast(s) for about 20 minutes, then take it off for about 20 minutes. The breaks 'wake up' your breasts and are more effective than steady cold.
- Use cabbage leaves to help bring down swelling – an old remedy in the 'can't hurt, might help' category. Discard the outer, possibly sprayed, leaves of a head of green cabbage. (Red cabbage could stain.) Now peel off one or more leaves, tear out the hard vein if you like, crumple each leaf gently in your hand, and put the leaves on your breast (not over your nipple). They should feel nice and cool,

and can be held in place with a bra or shirt. Leave them on until you get tired of them, and repeat as often as you like. Maybe there's a reason cabbage leaves are shaped the way they are!

⊿ Stand in a shower and let the hot water land between your shoulderblades. You may find yourself leaking in the shower. If not, it's still relaxing.

Consult your doctor if you're experiencing any symptoms of mastitis or you have any persistent new breast lumps.

DIASTASIS RECTI

When you're pregnant and your expanding tummy grows, your abdominal muscles begin to separate – a condition known as diastasis recti. Diastasis is anything over 2.7 centimetres of separation between the ab muscles. After birth the muscles will typically come back together, but up to one in three women can experience permanent separation. You can check to see if any separation remains by lying on your back with your knees bent and your feet flat on the floor. Lift your head and neck off the ground (try not to engage the core) and, using two fingers, press a line from your belly button up to the top of your tummy and then from your belly button down in a line to the bottom of your tummy. Diastasis recti (DR) is fairly easy to identify: it often feels like a 'hole' in your tummy around the belly button, or a crevice between the muscles when you press down. It will feel soft and your stomach can bulge outwards in a cone shape when you contract your abs (try not to allow that cone-shape bulge to happen, though, because that can make your DR worse). If you've tested your tummy and think you have DR, you may want to learn some very simple yet important ways to get up when lying down, to engage your core while picking up your kids and a safe way to sneeze to protect your stomach.

Sarah: I have experienced this with both of my pregnancies. I first discovered my diastasis recti when my tummy looked like a pyramid as I was trying to get up in a very unhealthy way off the floor. I worked on my separation, which was three fingers wide in the middle with my first, and four fingers wide in the middle with my second. The first thing I learned was that you need to get up out of bed or off the floor in a very different way. If lying on your back you turn to your side and push off the ground or bed with your hands, much like when you were pregnant. This will help prevent making your DR worse. The good news is there are amazing programs to help you. My absolute favourite website, app and workout series for pelvic floor and diastasis recti is Every Mother (every-mother.com). You can start Every Mother when you are pregnant to strengthen and support your pelvic floor, or you can pick it up postpartum. Every Mother's Prepare program for pregnancy 'will help you avoid common pregnancy discomforts, such as low back pain and urinary incontinence, as you safely build strength and stamina for birth'. I also love Aussie-born mama Ali Handley from bodylove-pilates.com. She has created a beautiful program specific to helping expectant and postpartum mothers repair, recover and thrive.

There are a number of wonderful exercises you can do to help bring your abs back together again. In addition to the curated DR program from Every Mother, physiotherapist Michelle Kenway from pelvicexercises.com.au has shared two of her favourite DR support exercises below.

DIASTASIS RECTI EXERCISE 1

ACTIVATING THE DEEP ABDOMINAL MUSCLES

LYING ON YOUR SIDE.

Start by lying on your side.

Use your fingers to feel your abdominal wall just inside your pelvic bone.

Activate your lower abdominal wall by gently drawing inwards the area beneath your briefs.

Maintain this abdominal activation for up to 10 seconds.

Breathe normally throughout.

Relax your abdominal wall back to resting.

NOTE: Your upper abdomen should remain relaxed throughout this exercise.

PROGRESSION

Start by learning to correctly activate your deep abdominal muscles before extending the duration of this hold for up to 10 seconds at a time.

DIASTASIS RECTI EXERCISE 2

ACTIVATING THE DEEP ABDOMINAL MUSCLES LYING FLAT.

Start by lying on your back.

Bend your knees and keep your feet flat.

Maintain the normal inward curve in your lower back throughout.

Place your fingers on your lower abdominal wall just inside your pelvic bone.

Gently activate your deep abdominal muscles (use the same technique as in exercise 1).

Maintain this abdominal activation for up to 10 seconds.

Breathe normally throughout.

Relax your abdominal wall back to resting.

NOTE: Your upper abdomen should remain relaxed throughout this exercise.

PROGRESSION

Start out by learning to correctly activate your deep abdominal muscles before extending the duration of this hold for up to 10 seconds at a time.

THE FIRST FORTY DAYS

The first forty days is a concept we came across in the book *The First Forty Days: The Essential Art of Nourishing the New Mother* by Heng Ou, Amely Greeven and Marisa Belger. The book focuses on the idea that in many societies around the world, from Japan to Korea to Latin America, the first forty days post birth is a time of transition, learning, recovery and rest for the new mother. Within this period the new mother is nurtured by friends and family, cooked for, pampered and taken care of so she can stay homebound, tend to herself and focus solely on connecting with and nourishing her new baby. (The book also includes some amazing healing recipes for mama.)

It is time to change our ways, to pick up the threads of knowledge that we forgot and weave them into a new kind of fabric to hold the mother. It is time to reclaim the postpartum period and reinstate it to its rightful place as the important conclusion of the childbearing story, something that deserves as much forethought as pregnancy and birth. We must do it for ourselves and for our children, because the way women become mothers profoundly affects the way their children awaken to this world. When you take care of the mother, you take care of the child.

—THE FIRST FORTY DAYS

We celebrate and advocate for this kind of recovery period and we both practised versions of it (one of us more than the other – Sarah!). It's completely understandable that for many second, third or fourth-time mums it can be difficult to wrap your head around the idea of staying at home bonding with your new baby for forty days when it seems like there's so much to get done. Not to mention the mummy guilt that kicks in when you're so focused on the new baby and not their older sibling(s)! So, find a happy medium if that speaks more to you, but just remember that taking more of a rest than you might initially intend in those first six weeks is highly beneficial – not just for your body, but for your mind and your baby too. As we spoke about in Chapter 1, now is the time to lean on your key support people. Remember, it takes a village.

SIX WEEKS POSTPARTUM AND BEYOND

As your body and hormones start to regulate, you'll notice your shape changing. For some this happens rapidly, but for most it takes a while to feel like your old self again. Be easy on yourself, Mama! Your bod is still going to be holding extra weight. It might look very stretched out or a bit puffy, and you'll probably still look pregnant – this is totally normal, and even though the length of time varies, rest assured it happens to every new mama. You might notice wiry hair and dark circles under your eyes, or maybe your skin is looking a little grey due to the crazy hormone fluctuations. Yes, this is postpartum life: lots of adjustments and changes. You won't look the same as you did before. It will come in time, or it might not, but either way your amazing body carried and birthed your baby. Stretch marks are your battle wounds and cellulite reminds us of all we went through to bring our babes earthside. We unite as mothers with our shapely bodies, leaky boobs, our wrinkly, squishy bellies for our children to curl up on and our warm, safe, loving hands to hold them. That's a body to be celebrated.

Teresa: I lost my 'baby weight' relatively quickly the first two times around, but after my third I still have 'the pooch' they talk about. One of my favourite things to do is smoosh my tummy up like an old withered peach and show my kids how cool it is that my stomach can do this all because I carried them in there. I also sprouted ALL the greys after Forest's birth, my hair has tons of them now, but luckily, I can laugh it off and keep telling myself those greys are 'mum chic'. I've also noticed the lighting crew on the TV show I'm currently on use a truckload of white reflector boards to try and brighten the black holes that sit permanently under my eyes. My character is an early thirties childless woman, who should look a little fresher than this mama of three. I felt a pang of self-consciousness, but there's nothing I'm more proud of than my role as a mother, so I will happily take the bags, melasma, greys, wrinkles and new softness any day. I look at my body as this fierce thing capable of carrying and birthing babies. I'm in awe of it.

Sarah: With my first I felt like the baby weight came off in the first nine months. My tummy always had a pooch but that was from my diastasis recti and the fact that I'd carried such a large baby. With my second child I was in the midst of shooting a movie. We had finished the film before I fell pregnant but needed to go back and do additional photography after the baby was born. I felt nervous about trying to get back into my pre-pregnancy costumes, and I remember buying loads of Spanx, but when I spoke to the person in wardrobe, she told me to stop worrying and that they would just add material to my dresses if needed. I gave away loads of pants that I knew belonged to a body of my past. I'm okay with that though, and I agree with Teresa – I am grateful for my health and strength, and in awe of my body's ability to carry, give birth to and nurse two babies.

It's important to ensure you are eating a balanced diet with plenty of whole foods, fruits and veggies plus protein. Quinoa and nut butters are good plant-based sources, or if you're a meat eater salmon is a great source of protein, plus it's packed full of omega-3 fatty acids. If you're breastfeeding make sure you're taking in enough calories and replenishing your body so you don't get run down. Maternal depletion is a real thing – breastfeeding places high demands on maternal stores and protein. Your partner and support crew (family and friends) should understand the importance of mama's nutrition. That way if you forget to tend to your own needs because you're busy focusing on baby, they can ensure that you're drinking plenty of fluids and eating some hearty, nutrient-dense meals.

MAKING LUUURVE

If you're feeling frisky, the great news is that after six weeks most people will get the all-clear to have sex again. A lot of healthcare providers advise waiting four to six weeks after delivery before having sex (regardless of the delivery method). But every recovery is unique, so ask your doctor to give you a check-up before you decide.

Make sure you have birth control sorted, too, as some women can get pregnant after just giving birth. (Typically, breastfeeding acts as a pretty good contraceptive but this is NOT foolproof!) Having sex for the first time after giving birth can feel a little tender, so take it easy, but there shouldn't usually be anything that feels too uncomfortable. If it's painful, speak to your care provider.

Sarah: My postpartum doula the first time around said something that should be obvious but wasn't so obvious in my postpartum haze. She said, you don't have to have intercourse to have sex. Point being, if you are feeling it in your body but not so ready to go all the way to home base, take a trip back to your dating days and explore allll the bases.

GETTING MOVING AGAIN

We partnered with Tammy Obst for this section. Tammy, a pre- and post-natal exercise specialist trainer based in Adelaide, has been in the health and fitness industry for over 8 years.

The recovery of a woman post baby depends on many variables and it can be overwhelming to work out where to begin the process. Your body has undergone a birth marathon, and no matter how your beautiful child was born it is important to be patient and give your self time to heal and re-strengthen. Moving can be a good way to get out of the house, clear your head and stop you from feeling isolated. It helps your body to repair, increases your endorphins and can help you feel positive about yourself. Here are some slow steps you can take.

BIRTH – WEEK 3

Start with slow 10–15 minute walks. Gradually build up the duration.

Start doing diaphragmatic breathing (breathing into your stomach rather than your chest) in bed before you go to sleep as your diaphragm has been impacted during pregnancy.

Start doing short, basic pelvic floor contractions 3 times per day, while lying, sitting and standing.

Increase your walking duration to over 30 minutes, if it feels okay.

Choose 3 daily tasks (such as cleaning, doing dishes, showering) and spend two minutes during this time doing diaphragmatic breathing (to create a regular habit). This will assist your pelvic floor and core repair.

Commence three pelvic floor lifting positions per day to build up endurance.

WEEK 6

After a 6-week check-up with your Ob-Gyn you can usually resume low impact exercise.

Commence 30 minutes low impact cardio 3–5 times per week.

Begin more advanced pelvic floor and core strength exercises.

C—SECTION BIRTH

BIRTH — WEEK 6

Listen to your body and take things slowly.

To get up out of bed, roll onto your side and push yourself up to a seated position.

Commence diaphragmatic breathing; this will begin repair of core and initiate the activation of your pelvic floor.

Start taking short walks with regulated diaphragmatic breathing (this will naturally relax and activate through the pelvic floor while walking).

6-WEEK CHECK-UP ONWARDS

Once you have had your 6-week check-up and have approval from your medical professional you can commence core, pelvic floor and glute strength exercises.

Try wearing recovery compression shorts to offer some support.

Start scar tissue massage once healing has begun, usually after 8 weeks.

— TAMMY OBST, TAMMYOBST.COM

ZEN NOTES

- Be patient with your physical appearance and try to steer clear of comparison-itis. You'll be navigating immense changes, so expect the unexpected and embrace the gift your body has given you.

- You will have days when you feel like shit, look like shit, and will probably be covered in it, too. Welcome to the mums' club!

- Do the diastasis recti check!

- Your lady bits have taken a beating, so we recommend not looking down there any time soon!

- There will be blood, but remember: large clots or heavy bleeding warrants a call to your care provider.

- Your placenta is magical – figure out your placenta-plan!

- Your boobs will swell, leak and hurt, but hey, for those who've always wanted them, now you've got them. Boobalicious!

- Let your loved ones take care of you for the next three months – your new mantra is less is more. That goes for C-section mamas in particular: remember, you've just had major surgery!

YOUR MIND

SIX

Before you had your baby, you probably had an idea about what the experience might be like, and you know what? It's okay if it's different from what was in your mind. Perhaps it's harder, perhaps it's more beautiful; either way, you cannot underestimate the toll pregnancy, birth and new parenthood can take on your overall wellbeing. This stage can be challenging – all new things start off with a learning curve and this is no different. We've talked about some of the physical aspects of post-birth recovery, but it's also important to consider what you may be feeling and thinking, too – not least because the two can be closely interlinked.

We'll get onto some of the practicalities of caring for your new baby in the next chapter, but for now, remember that you know your baby better than any book, relative or well-meaning friend does. Trust your intuition and let go of any need to always get things right. It's time to embrace the imperfection of all that parenting brings. Let's talk about how you can look after your mind during this period.

The question each parent must keep alive as we raise our children is, 'How do I care well for myself, so that I can care well for them?' Adults, too, need good solid sleep, nourishing food, enough exercise and a sense of purpose in life. Each parent has to find her own way, and create rhythms for herself, just as we create them for our children. This is not a luxury; it is a job requirement.

—SHARIFA OPPENHEIMER, *HEAVEN ON EARTH*

THE FIRST MOMENTS FOLLOWING BIRTH

In the initial hours (and even days) after giving birth, you'll probably be feeling pretty overwhelmed, and in a state of awe, shock, elation, depletion and exhaustion. Many women talk about floating through this time in a haze, and sometimes this means it can take longer than you'd expect to connect and bond with your baby. Feeling sad or disconnected is completely understandable and normal. Be patient with yourself: you've just gone through a life-changing experience that is both physically and mentally taxing. It can take time to adjust. The good news is your body naturally makes a hormone called oxytocin, sometimes referred to as 'the love hormone' – it's released during childbirth, breastfeeding and sex! Along with its many other purposes, oxytocin helps your uterus contract during and post birth, helps bring your milk in when your baby begins to suckle and encourages connection and bonding between you and your baby.

BABY BLUES

If you feel anxious or overwhelmed, or experience teariness and mood swings after giving birth, know that you are not alone. There are mothers (and fathers too!) all over the world feeling stuck, sad and unsure about being a parent. You might feel particularly weepy, and as the fear of the unknown sets in you may find yourself thinking, 'What has happened to my life?' According to the Royal Women's

Hospital in Melbourne, up to 80 per cent of mothers suffer some form of baby blues. Having mild ups and downs for a couple of days or a couple of weeks comes with the territory.

Hormonal dips and shifts are the biggest contributor to these feelings. Your levels of oestrogen and progesterone rapidly drop after delivery, and these fluctuating hormones, combined with a lack of sleep, can really make things tough. You may feel like you're on a rollercoaster: high one minute and low the next. Many women report feeling particularly down on day three. Your feelings should start to regulate after a week or so, but if these oscillating emotions start feeling worse instead of better, and continue past two weeks, you may be experiencing postpartum depression or anxiety (see more about that below).

BABY BRAIN

Research tells us that having a baby is one of the most profound biological experiences a person can have, and one that radically affects your brain. A study published in 2016 states that pregnancy causes long-lasting changes in the human brain structure, particularly losses of the grey matter in the hippocampus, the area of our brain that's responsible for memory function, learning and emotions.[1] This study provides an insight into why we feel a bit off, foggy, scattered and forgetful during pregnancy and postpartum: our grey matter may not be fully restored until up to two years postpartum – sometimes even longer.

Sarah: I hit some lows in the first week after giving birth to Esmé. I was in pain, exhausted, and feeling guilty when my toddler wanted me to play with him and I couldn't. He was having a hard time understanding why Mummy was in bed for days. It was so weird for him, and made him act out. I felt like my relationship with him was going to change, and that I was losing this special bond that we have. Reflecting on my thoughts and feelings about three weeks postpartum,

I realised how short that period was, and how important it was for me to bond with my new baby. I was flooded with emotion and I know it was part of my hormonal dip. This came around day 5 postpartum, and then again around day 10. I later found out that day 5 is one of the hardest days for postpartum. I talked to Eric about my feelings and fears, and to some of my friends. It's important to check in with yourself during this time. And remember: the better we care for ourselves, the better we can care for our little ones.

If you're having feelings that overwhelm you, are having mood swings or panic attacks, or you just feel emotionally fragile, it's important to communicate that. Confide in your partner, midwife, good friend or any other trusted person to help you through. You could also try a natural approach to see if you notice a change in your moods. Here are a few ideas.

- Take herbs that help boost serotonin levels in your brain and tackle anxiety. We love supportive herbs such as St John's wort, lemon balm, passionflower and hops tea. Please ask your doctor before having herbs while breastfeeding or taking any other medications.
- Meditation. Studies have shown that meditation in the form of mindfulness-based cognitive therapy (MBCT) can be highly beneficial in treating depression.
- Get moving. Exercise releases the feel-good hormones in your brain.
- Vitamin D. Standing out in the sunshine triggers positive emotions in your brain.
- Omega-3s. Eat some fatty salmon or avocados. Omega-3s are directly related to proper brain function.

WHEN YOUR LOWS FEEL TOO LOW

If your sadness feels really intense and it's lasting longer than two weeks, it's time to reach out to your health care professional or a therapist. Perinatal anxiety and depression can occur at any point from pregnancy throughout the first year postpartum and for a multitude of reasons. There is also a lot of overlap between the two. For example, at five or six months your little one is being introduced to solid food and sleeping longer stretches of time at night. Both of these changes to your baby's habits cause your milk level to dip, which is a common reason for your hormones to be affected.

You may feel very alone, but the truth is, you're not – postpartum depression affects at least one in seven mothers, and postpartum anxiety affects one in five. Partners can be affected, too – according to panda.org.au (a wonderful source for anything to do with postpartum depression and anxiety), an estimated one in ten new fathers/partners will navigate depression and/or anxiety after the birth of their baby.

SIGNS AND SYMPTOMS OF POSTPARTUM DEPRESSION

Mood: anger, anxiety, guilt, hopelessness, loss of interest or pleasure in activities, mood swings or panic attacks

Behavioural: crying, irritability or restlessness

Whole body: fatigue or loss of appetite

Cognitive: lack of concentration or unwanted thoughts

Psychological: depression or fear

Weight: weight gain or weight loss

Also common: insomnia or repeatedly going over thoughts[2]

SIGNS AND SYMPTOMS OF POSTPARTUM ANXIETY

Mood: stressed, irritable, withdrawn, panic attacks

Behavioural: isolating oneself from social situations, irritability, over
controlling, manipulating, restlessness, asking for constant reassurance

Whole body: heart racing, sweating, shallow breathing, muscle tension

Cognitive: racing thoughts, obsessing over the future, morbid thinking,
ruminating, worrying

Psychological: difficulty sleeping, fear

Weight: weight gain or weight loss

Also common: loss of appetite

Teresa: My husband, Mark, had postpartum anxiety in the first few days after Poet's birth. It was the first time we'd navigated baby blues. He was irritable, afraid, teary and so worried about Poet that he didn't like anyone but me touching her. Looking back on that time now, we believe a lot of it stemmed from lack of sleep and Mark's feelings about having a daughter after three sons, which made him instinctively over-protective. We worked through this by ensuring that we were 'housing in', keeping our space sacred and limiting visitors. Mark also resumed his daily meditation practice.

THERE'S LIGHT AT THE END OF THE TUNNEL

There are many ways to treat postnatal depression and anxiety, and it's important to remember that this too shall pass. Both are usually temporary – you won't always feel this heavy.

Talk to your health care provider to come up with a plan of attack. If you think you may be experiencing postpartum depression you can also call the Perinatal Anxiety & Depression Australia (PANDA) Helpline on 1300 726 306.

Sarah: My father was dying during my pregnancy with Esmé. It was a very vulnerable time where I was taking care of him, helping my mother, plus trying to take care of myself and the little one inside of me. I was terrified that the overwhelmingly sad feelings I was experiencing would have a negative effect on me and my baby. I reached out to Dr Alyssa Berlin at the Berlin Wellness Center in the US as she specialises in prenatal and postpartum therapy. (You can find prenatal and postpartum therapists who specialise in postpartum depression and anxiety.) Just talking to her and having time to sort out all of my feelings during pregnancy and postpartum helped lighten the weight I was carrying.

Weeks after my daughter was born, out of nowhere, I found myself crying while breastfeeding in the middle of the night. I felt so in love with my daughter but I was sad and missing my dad. I would also feel anxious and scared watching my daughter breathe at night, praying that she would be safe and nothing would happen to her. Being able to talk to someone about my fears and my sadness supported me and made me feel safe.

CALL ON YOUR COMMUNITY

Now is the time to engage the help of your sisterhood! Those of your friends who have already experienced mamahood may be particularly helpful, as they have been in the trenches themselves. Use them as a shoulder to cry on, arms to hold your baby while you shower, nap or read a book, and ears to listen to your complaints, fears and worries. Sometimes having someone listen with empathy can be all you need to regulate your emotions.

LOOK ONLINE

Finding a supportive online community is another great option. Whether it's a 'midnight mums' Facebook group, a new parents' forum or the honest, inspiring mamas you follow on Instagram, there is something beautiful about finding common ground with strangers from all over the globe. That's one of the main reasons we created *Your Zen Mama*: we wanted a hub where people could receive support, feel held and uplifted, forge friendships and have a voice to share their experiences. There are many conflicting voices out there and lots of people ready to give advice, which at times can be overwhelming. Just try to keep yourself away from the negative energy and focus on the topics and groups that make you feel good, safe and supported.

RECEIVING VISITORS

Friends and family are fantastic but they can get pretty pumped about a new baby, and sometimes they forget to think about what the new parents *really* need: rest and help. If they're popping over, they should be making your life easier in some way while they're there.

Everyone means well but many unintentionally overstep boundaries – including how long they should stay! Davi Khalsa, the midwife we used with our first babies, suggested writing a note for keen visitors and placing it on the front door. You could try something like this:

For the health of our new baby, please take the time to wash your hands before entry, and take off your shoes. Since we are sleep deprived, covered in poop, vomit and other bodily fluids, and so clearly looking and feeling like our best selves, please keep your visits to 30 minutes maximum (unless changing nappies, holding baby while we finally get to shower, throwing a load of washing on, cooking for us, doing the dishes, mopping floors or changing the sheets . . .) Please and thank you! Love from Baby Wyatt's overwhelmed parents.

Limiting visitors is something to think about, too. There is just so much to wrap your head around; you need a chance to recalibrate without having to be social. Sometimes overzealous grandparents can overstep boundaries, imparting all their 'wisdom' on what the new parents should be doing. The last thing you need is to feel as though you're under scrutiny, so try to ensure that both you and your partner are able to speak up when you need to.

> **Teresa:** I have a unique situation with my mum: she is super gentle, loving and very passive. For the birth of all three of my babies, I had Mum living with us for the first eight weeks – she's on her own, retired and just craves being with us, so it has been a win-win for all. When we had Bodhi, she would get up with him at 6.30 am and have cuddle time while we caught up on sleep. With Forest she helped around the house while I bonded with him, and most recently, with Poet, she has been all over the washing, plus keeping the older kids entertained. She is a godsend and I'm so glad that my children's nanna was around so much in the first few months of their lives.

MOTHERS' GROUPS

Something that really helped us as new mums was joining a local mothers' group. Typically, each class is led by a childcare or parenting professional, who will discuss new topics from week to week. These classes allow you and the other new mothers to share experiences and ask questions. If something like this is available in your community it can be a brilliant way to meet new mamas and also talk to a professional about your experiences. It's a beautiful way to connect and feel heard on subjects that may otherwise make you feel very alone. Topics might include: breastfeeding, night feeding, parenting with your partner, functioning on little to no sleep, establishing 'me time' and helping baby to sleep. We both learned so much about ourselves, our babies and what kind of parents we wanted to be from these classes. They allowed us to share and experiment with different techniques, plus meet other mamas on the same journey. We both still have close friends we made from those very first few weeks of class.

POSTPARTUM DOULAS

Another support option that's becoming popular is a postpartum doula. Postpartum doulas exist to serve the mother, creating an environment in which she can be nurtured and taken care of. This support and reassurance can be particularly helpful for mamas whose partners must return to work soon after the baby's birth and who don't have a 'village' nearby to turn to. Postpartum doulas' services include cooking meals, doing the washing, cleaning dishes and holding your baby so you can take a nap or have a bath (they won't offer medical advice, though; your maternal and child health nurse should do this).

Sarah: I'd never even heard of a postpartum doula. When my birth doula asked me what my postpartum plan was, I told her I'd be taking care of my baby and Eric would help when he was home – my husband was working five days a week, sometimes sixteen hours a day, when our son was due. She wisely suggested I meet some postpartum doulas so I'd have some help in place for a couple of weeks postpartum. When I met Janet, I clicked with her straight away, and it turned out I needed her more than I ever imagined. In giving birth to Wyatt I popped a rib and had trouble even picking him up for about two weeks. Janet came a few days a week and would hold Wyatt, do laundry, cook food for me and make sure I was eating, help me with breastfeeding and answer all the 10 000 questions I had. It was the greatest gift, and I am forever grateful that I was able to have her.

In Australia, postpartum doulas generally visit just once a week, or a few times in total. You can research recommended postpartum doulas in your area online (try douladirectory.com.au). They may charge an hourly rate somewhere between $25–110[3], depending on their experience. The Australian Doula College has a charity arm, The Doula Heart Network, which offers free postpartum care for at risk or in need parents.

SELF-CARE

Self-care is a very buzzy term at the moment, and for good reason. Psychologists tell us that 'me time' helps boost our concentration, regulates our emotions, aids in problem solving, reboots our brains and helps to lower stress. A new baby can feel all-consuming, especially as it's such a round-the-clock experience. It can be good to remind yourself that you existed as an individual long before your baby did – and you *do* still have that identity. We often get so tied into our new role as parents that we lose sight of all the things that make us unique. Giving yourself a little individualised attention will make it easier to connect back into yourself! Remember, to be the best mum and person you can be, both for yourself and that new little ball of cuteness, you're going to need time out on a regular basis. This motherhood business is a marathon, not a sprint!

When you have one hour to spare:

- Take a yin yoga class
- Soak in a bath (use those bath salts you were given at your baby shower!)
- Listen to your favourite podcast
- Go have a cup of coffee with a friend
- Take a leisurely stroll and listen to music
- Take yourself out for a kid-free lunch
- Spend time at the gym
- Get a massage
- Have a facial
- Go shopping
- Read a book
- Netflix and chill
- Bake some sugary desserts for later consumption!

When you have twenty minutes to spare:

- Take a drive and listen to your favourite music
- Take a walk around the block
- Immerse yourself in nature with a walk down a leafy street or at a nearby park
- Get a mani or a pedi
- FaceTime a friend
- Peruse a favourite blog
- Do a guided meditation (try an app like Insight Timer)
- Watch some postpartum vlogs (you can find some of ours on yourzenmama.com!)
- Write in a journal – it's always so helpful to get your thoughts out on paper
- Drink a glass of wine or a relaxing cup of tea in a cozy spot

SAY NO TO SOCIAL COMPARISONS

We all do it: compare ourselves to what we perceive other people's experiences to be. As Eckhart Tolle would say, it's another way to keep you in your 'pain-body', the part of yourself that dips into old emotional pain out of habit. The pain-body thrives on social media and our perfectionist culture, filled with flattering images of 'flawless' postpartum bods and happy, cooing babies. There is room for that, and we're not here to criticise those posts (we love looking at them, and have posted our own versions of them too) but it's important to remember that they aren't showing the *whole* picture. What did it look like when that family first woke up in the morning? When they were tantrum taming, and frantically getting everyone fed, dressed and out the door on time? Were there clothes thrown about, dishes in the sink and days-old washing stuffed in the bottom of the laundry basket?

Are those real-life moments harder to capture because they're stressful or are they simply something that we do not want to shine a light on? Those moments can be beautiful too, though, and the truth is we all have them – even the perfectly plaited, monochromatic, spotless mum you love to follow. The in-between moments are messy for us all. Comparison is human nature, but when your hormones are running rampant, it makes everything feel more *ugh*.

To avoid these comparisons, take a social media hiatus until you feel confident that others' posts won't trigger you into a state of comparison. Alternatively, mute any social media profiles that aren't currently serving you. Instead, look out for pages where folks are being open, vulnerable and real about their experiences, showing all sides of their journey.

This goes for your community offline, too: be selective about the people you spend time with until you feel content with your own situation. Work on reminding yourself how strong, amazing and capable you are every day.

Teresa: I'm often asked by journalists why I choose to be so revealing in my public profile. There are very specific reasons why I choose to be so open. I want to use my platform to help create change, and my area of passion is stripping down the barriers between people and highlighting the common threads that bind us. So many of life's hard journeys are hurdles we all navigate. Sharing vulnerabilities and challenges as well as moments of celebration is important to me because I celebrate and respect realness, and my industry in particular feeds a false sense of reality. I firmly believe that the more we all can share our truths, the less alone we feel.

AND FINALLY: YOUR BABES WILL GROW AND SO WILL YOU

A common phrase we hear is, 'The days are long but the years are short.' These long, sleepy, cuddly newborn days (and nights) might become memories you look back upon with great fondness (there *is* a reason mums go back again for more babes!). Before you know it you'll be folding up the itty bitty newborn onesies and marvelling at how fleeting those early days were. So, try to remind your 3 am self, who's covered in vomit, massaging swollen boobs and drenched in sweat: these twelve or so weeks won't last, and your life will find balance in time.

Right, now let's talk about baby!

ZEN NOTES

↘ It is completely normal to feel like you're on an upside-down rollercoaster –
you're not losing your marbles, you're just losing sleep and your hormones
are dropping!

↘ Talk to your partner, girlfriends, parents and siblings or a professional
if it's all getting too much. Don't be afraid to ask for help, and definitely do
after the two-week mark if you still feel blue.

↘ Get off the 'gram, or at least mute the (well-meaning) Stepford wives
until you're feeling better.

↘ Remember, taking care of yourself will make for a healthier, more level-
headed mama.

YOUR BABY

SEVEN

What a smooshy little ball of love, poo and tears you now have! It's kind of crazy when you suddenly find yourself with this teeny little thing and you're expected to know exactly how to take care of it. But don't worry, your mama instincts are strong and loud – you just need to listen to them.

FIRST MOMENTS

In uncomplicated births, once your baby is born, they will be placed on your chest and covered with a blanket so you can cuddle together, skin on skin. The benefits of skin-on-skin time with your newborn are plentiful: it promotes both temperature and blood sugar regulation, provides a comforting and safe spot for baby to nestle in after the rigorous experience of birth, and helps to encourage breastfeeding (more on this below). Gone are the days of washing babies straight after birth: these days, medical professionals understand the value of leaving the vernix on babies' bodies and all the goodness it brings them. Vernix can act as a wonderful barrier against infections, is the world's best moisturiser and imparts antimicrobial properties.

If any complications have arisen during birth, your babe may be taken to be assessed and monitored in the Special Care Nursery or the Neonatal Intensive Care Unit. Various tests may be performed, and while these can be very worrying and stressful, your baby's health care team will keep you up to date.

Teresa: About a minute after Forest's birth, my midwife, Julie, noticed that he went limp for a moment on my chest. His Apgar was 5. Julie kept very calm, telling me to rub his back and talk to him. She then scooped him up, the cord was cut and the staff alerted. Julie took Forest over to the monitoring area for some oxygen as the neonatal doctor came in. It was all done so swiftly and considerately to avoid startling me, and I felt confident that he was okay, as I could see how pink (and big!) he looked. I was so thankful that no one went into a panic, and for the respectful communication and soothing responses to my questions. He was taken to the neonatal unit for a couple of hours' observation, then after his first breastfeed and another half-hour of monitoring, we were able to leave the hospital.

You can ask for most checks to be done while baby is on your chest, including the all-important Apgar test: an evaluation of the baby's wellbeing at around one minute and then five minutes post birth. Your baby's Apgar score is determined by looking at five specific areas: heart rate, respiration, muscle tone, reflex response and colour. Your baby is given a score between 0 and 2 for each of these areas, with the highest and most favourable overall score being 10 (note, most babies will not receive a 10 on their first Apgar test). Your baby will also be given a hospital tag to identify them and will be weighed shortly after birth to determine their birth weight. If vitamin K is being administered, this will happen within the first 24 hours – it's an important step to ensure your baby doesn't have any unexpected bleeding. Your midwife, doctor or nurse will also prick your baby's heel in order to collect a blood sample, which is used to test for a variety of metabolic diseases. Other common procedures within the first 24 hours are the hepatitis B vaccination and (if you're in the US) eye drops to prevent eye infections. Speak with your doctor or midwife to learn more about these procedures and to inform your decisions.

Within a couple of days of birth, your baby will also be given a hearing test. Many babies fail the first one (as Poet did) – don't panic. Pro tip: clear the room so it's quiet (and sibling-free). Feed baby until they are full, peaceful and happy, making them more likely to keep still, but then take them off the breast before testing – the sucking motions, related nursing sounds and yummy milk they're ingesting could distract them from the beeps involved in the test, leading to a false negative result.

THE FIRST WEEK

Many people describe the first week as a total blur. There will be no semblance of a routine at this age – the days will be completely different – but typically your little baby will be asleep most of the time. In the week after birth, babies tend to sleep an average of 18 hours a day, which is great because it means YOU can also rest. Often your baby will mix up their days and nights which can throw a spanner in the works. We talk more below about helping your baby separate day from night.

'Freshies' (as we like to call them) crave being held, snuggled and comforted. It's pretty much impossible to spoil babies this young! They need touch and warmth – that, along with the sustenance they get from your milk, is how they thrive. They've just been expelled from the womb and thrust into this huge new existence, so naturally they want to be close to you. They can recognise your voice and your smell, and your touch makes them feel safe.

THE NEW DYNAMIC WITH OLDER SIBLINGS

If this new baby is not your first, you might be wondering how your other children will adjust. Older children are naturally very excited, but also sometimes anxious about having a new sibling. Even very young children will often sense that big change is coming. It's also quite normal for older children to have a slight regression in the form of altered sleep, bed wetting or acting out for attention. Things *will* settle down, it just takes some time for them to get used to the new normal.

Here are some ways to help with that big transition.

- It's a lovely idea to buy a present from the baby for their new big brother or sister. This can help put the baby in their good books (for a while at least!).

- Ask visiting friends and family if they wouldn't mind giving a present to the older child too, if they're bringing something for the new baby, so they don't feel left out.

- Give your other children responsibilities with the baby. Ask them, 'What do you think baby needs?' or encourage them: 'Yes, you're right – you know baby so well!'

- Wear your baby (more on this below) so you're more able to meet the needs of toddlers and older sibs, keeping things familiar.

- Remind your older child to have soft hands with the baby. Be mindful to encourage their interest, though, and avoid scolding them by constantly saying 'Don't touch' or 'Be gentle'.

- If your next eldest child is still on the younger side and you've been breastfeeding them through this pregnancy, perhaps consider tandem nursing for the first few months. This should help reduce sibling jealousy.

WHAT YOU *REALLY* NEED IN THE FIRST WEEKS

When you get pregnant you'll hear about all the 'must-have' items you'll need for your baby. A lot of people blow huge amounts of money on buying *all the things*. But babies don't need as much as you think, and some of the things they need are only required for a very brief stint (i.e. a lie-flat pram cocoon). Here's a list of what we think you'll really need:

- Nappies and wipes
- Burp cloths (ten is a good number)
- Baby carrier

- Car seat
- Sleeping bassinet (it's great if it's on wheels or easily moveable into other rooms for daytime naps)
- Zip-up swaddles (about 5–7 will do)
- Easy access onesies with two zips for changing nappies (about ten; we like ones made from organic fabrics if possible)
- Lightweight blankets/receiving blankets (about five)
- Baby swing (soooo handy for taking a bath or just having a break! Look out for reasonably priced secondhand ones)
- Barrier cream
- White clay powder (organic if possible)
- Baby shampoo/wash (organic if possible)
- Small easy-to-travel pram (aim to get one that suits babies from 5 months onwards – it'll last you longer than a newborn/lie-down one)

When buying baby clothes, make sure you only get a few items for the newborn stage – they grow out of those tiny sizes so quickly! Sizes 0–3 and 3–6 months are more practical. Another fab idea is to use friends' hand-me-downs and have a bunch of clothes in rotation among a group of you. It's very sweet to see your friends' babes re-wearing clothes your darling has grown out of. Plus, it's better for the environment.

BREASTFEEDING

Breastfeeding is considered best for your baby because breastmilk is basically nature's perfect food, offering the ideal nutrition for newborns. It has other health benefits for babies, too, helping to prevent ear infections, viruses and respiratory tract infections and promote easier digestion. That said, it's not the only feeding option, as we'll discuss a little later on.

Breastfeeding can be a beautiful experience between mother and child, but it doesn't always come easily or naturally. It's a learning process and a skill you'll need to develop – something a lot of new mamas don't realise – so being well informed and supported is key. We highly recommend some reading on the topic during your third trimester. For us, *The Womanly Art of Breastfeeding* was a mother's breast friend (pardon the pun!). Familiarise yourself with some of the recommended positions and latching techniques – being equipped with information will empower you.

ESTABLISHING A LATCH

The very first breastfeed is a special experience. Soon after birth you'll notice that your baby will begin to root and suck, which is an indication that they're ready to suckle at your breast. This rooting action happens at its peak intensity around 45 minutes post birth, with baby sucking on their little fists, moving their head side to side and rubbing their mouth on your skin, searching for your breast. This is referred to as 'the breast crawl'. The mama's smell helps the baby to instinctively seek out her nipple, which is believed to secrete an odour that baby finds appealing. Babies will use their stepping reflex to push against mama's tummy with their legs, making small push-up motions to get closer to the nipple. Your areola will most likely have darkened during pregnancy, making it easier for baby to see their target. You can aid your baby along to the breast if you wish, or let them find their way organically – it's up to you!

Although our little ones instinctively know how to feed, this doesn't mean the latch will immediately be perfect. Once you've established a latch, check to see if it feels comfortable, and if the baby's lip is underneath your areola. Baby should not just be sucking on the nipple, as that will cause you discomfort and set up a bad latch. The wider your baby's mouth is when coming to the breast, the easier it will be to feed more of your areola into their mouth. Aim to get the whole thing in – that way at least a fair portion of the areola will be inside their mouth, along with the nipple, which should be sitting towards the back of baby's mouth. Sometimes pinching your areola between two fingers and feeding it into baby's mouth will help baby get a better latch. Before leaving the birth centre or hospital, have your latch checked out, ideally by someone experienced with breastfeeding positions and techniques, such as the resident lactation consultant.

Here is some more information on establishing the right latch used by permission of La Leche League International:

When latching on your baby, use your nipple to tickle the center of your baby's bottom lip. This will encourage him to open his mouth wide (like he is yawning). Aim your nipple slightly towards the roof of his mouth, bringing baby to you, chin first.

Good latch-on checkpoints for your baby include:

⬎ His nose is nearly touching your breast, that is, no further away than a credit card edge.

⬎ His lips are flanged.

⬎ At least 1 centimetre of your breast around the base of your nipple is in his mouth.

⬎ If the latch is uncomfortable or painful, gently place your finger in the baby's mouth, between his gums, to detach him and try again.

⬎ A baby who is offered the breast will suck without swallowing as he positions the nipple in his mouth and tells your breast he is ready for the milk to let down.

⬎ When he begins to receive milk, you will see his jaw working all the way back to his ear. His temples will wiggle. You will also hear him swallowing, quickly at first, then more slowly, as his appetite is satisfied.

Even with a perfect latch, some women will still experience pain during breast-feeding. It's important to communicate your experiences to a lactation consultant, nurse or midwife who can help get you get off to the right start.

Some babies might be tongue-tied, which is when the baby's frenulum (the skin attaching the tongue to the bottom of the mouth) is too tight, thick or short, restricting their range of motion. Your paediatrician will tell you whether or not your baby has a tongue or lip tie, which can lead to a poor latch and result in cracked, bleeding nipples. There are easy and gentle ways of taking care of tongue-ties, which your doctor will discuss with you.

LIQUID GOLD

The first 'milk' your body produces is called colostrum, sometimes referred to as 'liquid gold' or 'golden milk'. This nutrient-rich liquid is what your baby drinks during the first few days before your milk comes in. Colostrum brings all sorts of benefits, including boosting baby's immune system, helping prevent jaundice, creating a coating for the stomach to fight germs and helping prevent low blood sugar.

MILK SUPPLY AND FREQUENCY OF BREASTFEEDING

The more you feed, the more milk you make! Our doctors recommended that we feed on demand, as high-frequency nursing can help increase milk supply.

Listen to your baby's needs, and act upon their hunger cues. You don't have to worry about overfeeding at this age, but you do have to worry about underfeeding. Underfeeding your baby can lead to brain injury[1], which is why it's important to ensure you're nursing at least ten times in 24 hours in the early days. If you see your baby sticking their tongue out of their mouth, sucking on their hands, moving their head from side to side and looking like they're bobbing for apples, then you know they're hungry. Basically, as soon as you have the inkling that babe is ready for milk, put them on the breast. Feed them unlimited amounts of milk until they decide they're finished – they'll let you know they're done by spitting the nipple out.

WHICH BOOB?

In the first couple of weeks it is recommended that you switch from breast to breast during each nursing session, as this helps stimulate milk production. After breastfeeding is well established, you can alternate breasts within a session. Despite what you may have heard, in our experience there's no need to note down which breast you used last – you'll be able to tell by how heavy each boob is! Just in case you do like to keep track there are great breastfeeding apps – Sarah used the Baby Feed Timer app with her first baby, Wyatt.

THE GASSY TUMMY

Oh, the dreaded gassy tummies! These can strike at any time and can interrupt sleep. Ensure that you're breastfeeding with baby's head higher than their tummy – this will prevent air bubbles getting trapped. When side lying and nursing, ensure that baby is at least on a slight angle with their tummy lower than their upper body.

Burping baby after a feed is also helpful. There are several techniques you can try. Some babies let out a loud belch if you prop them up looking over your shoulder and pat and rub them between the shoulder blades. Otherwise you can sit them on your lap, support their head and neck and lean them forwards in circular motions, switching between an anti-clockwise and clockwise direction. This is a great one to get some of the trickier air out, and is an old-school favourite of many midwives.

Other things that might help include:

- a tummy massage for baby (google the 'I love you' method)
- tummy time (the pressure helps force unwanted gas out!)

⊐ baby bike ride (pumping their legs in a bike-riding fashion helps relieve any gas bubbles that may be stuck).

HOW CAN YOU TELL IF BABY IS GETTING ENOUGH MILK?

It is normal for your baby to lose weight post-birth – most babies will lose about 225 grams off their birth weight. This is because mama's milk takes a few days to come in, and your freshie is born with extra fluid, which they generally lose during those first few days. The sweet colostrum bubba gets in the first few days of their life is incredibly beneficial for them, but as their tummies are so teeny they're only receiving about a teaspoon of colostrum per feed.

After your milk comes in your baby should start gaining weight. Most babies will be back up to their birth weight by around 10–14 days old. Your midwife or paediatrician will monitor whether your baby is making the appropriate gains, and they will be weighed during each check-up.

Your baby's poos and wees are a great indication of whether they're drinking enough milk. As a rule of thumb, before your milk comes in, baby should be having one wet nappy on the first day of life, two wet nappies on the second day, three wet nappies on the third day and so on until your milk has come in. After that, they should have at least five wet nappies daily. Poo should follow the same pre-milk ratio; once mama's milk is in, this should increase to a minimum of three bowel movements a day for the first several weeks, then decrease again – and they'll be a very different colour!

This leads us perfectly to poo! You're about to get up close and personal with your baby's poo – sometimes literally (even on your face!).

Your little sweetheart will have their first poop within twenty-four hours after birth. This poo will be greenish black and have a sticky, tar-like consistency. This is the baby's meconium! Baby will continue to poop this out until it's all out of their system. Then once your milk comes in, baby's poos will turn to a runnier, yellowish colour and the frequency of their bowel movements will increase. It's not uncommon for babes to poop after every nursing session. (We'll get onto nappies below . . .)

PUMPING AND TAKING THE BOTTLE

It's a good idea to wait until breastfeeding is fully established (usually around four to six weeks) before introducing a bottle, in order to help avoid nipple confusion. Nipple confusion is when baby unsuccessfully switches between bottle and breast, often resulting in them rejecting the nipple. Pumping is a great way of enabling your partner to take on nighttime feeding while you rest, giving your nipples a much-needed break, and it can be a godsend if you're going back to work. Pumping also helps boost your milk supply. Whatever the reason, there are amazing resources out there to support you through your pumping journey – La Leche League International (llli.org) is a good place to start.

It's important to pick the right bottle for your baby, and this will probably involve some trial and error. There are some great brands on the market that replicate the nipple and offer a smooth and continuous flow. When introducing a bottle to a breastfed baby, some specialists suggest using a preemie nipple on the bottle so that baby has to work to get the milk just like they do with the breast. Our favourites are Philips Avent, Baby Brezza and Dr Brown's with the preemie nipple.

Most breast pumps these days are very discreet, as well as being quick, quiet and easy-to-use. Some super fancy ones are even hands-free and wireless – though they come with a price tag! If you're in the market for one of these, the Elvie pump and the Willow are our picks. If you want a more cost-effective pump, the Medela is a very reliable and beloved brand. Alternatively, you can rent a pump from your hospital or lactation consultant. Some breast pump manufacturers also offer a rental service (Medela do).

BREASTFEEDING TOOLS

Breastfeeding is a bit of an exercise, but there are a few key items that can help. If you prefer to be discreet when breastfeeding in public, consider getting a nursing cover. Some babies won't like being under a blanket while nursing, but others will enjoy being distraction-free.

Another handy tool is a breastfeeding pillow. This can help keep you comfortable during longer breastfeeding sessions, and is especially handy for positioning. We both used one with our first babies while we were still getting the hang of things. We highly recommend the Boppy and the My Breast Friend pillow, which you can actually strap around you.

Certain styles of clothing can also make breastfeeding easier – it's all about easy access! Dresses with plunging necklines, button-down tops and stretchy T-shirts are all going in the yes pile, but skivvies and anything with a high neck (especially dresses) might end up in the no pile. Let's be real, these demanding little creatures won't want to wait while you're fussing with your clothes – no access, no good!

Another great asset will be a stash of nursing bras with clips for swift nursing. We are 'whip it out anywhere and everywhere' kinda gals – if baby is hungry and screaming for the boob, that trumps any semblance of modesty we ever had! If being more discreet is important to you then we suggest wearing a tank top under your clothes. You just pull your top shirt up and the tank top down, and your top shirt lies on top of any exposed cleavage. If a nursing blanket isn't for you, a scarf can be another great option, providing some coverage when you're among well-meaning strangers who like to stare at your little baby guzzling away.

WHEN BREASTFEEDING IS HARD

Most women find breastfeeding hard at some stage of their postpartum journey, and some women stop nursing because they don't have the right support. It's important to find peer encouragement. Chat to other mothers about their experiences, and ask your doctor or midwife for support and advice. You may also consider talking to or hiring a lactation consultant.

Some places will offer support over the phone, and attending a breastfeeding support group is also an option. These can be a great opportunity to meet other mothers navigating the same things you are. With the right support, encouragement and nurturing shown to you, many breastfeeding challenges can be overcome. It starts with you, though, Mama: being gentle, patient and kind to yourself during this sensitive period is paramount. Once it all clicks in, it'll flow (sorry, couldn't help ourselves!) and things will become much smoother.

Teresa: I met my entire friendship group of ten girlfriends out in LA at a mummy and me support group with my first son. I attended breastfeeding classes, baby and parent classes, music classes and more. I'm so grateful I was brave enough to attend these classes. I didn't know anyone else there, but I decided to take a leap of faith and go along. It was a game-changing decision that helped me find my community.

WHEN BREASTFEEDING ISN'T AN OPTION

Breastfeeding isn't always an option. Some women are on medication that isn't breastfeeding-friendly, some babies have physical issues that make breastfeeding difficult, some women have medical issues and are unable to nurse, and others have low milk supply or simply decide not to breastfeed. Whatever the reason, there are alternative options.

One alternative to mama's own milk is donated breastmilk. There are several milk banks operating around Australia though these organisations are mainly in place to provide donated milk to premature and sick babies in hospital. While there are many more options for sourcing regulated donor milk in the US, Australia is somewhat behind in terms of offering this as an official option for women who cannot or do not wish to breastfeed. Having said that, there are unofficial channels to source breastmilk. Two milksharing networks, Eats on Feets and Human Milk 4 Human Babies, link mothers willing to donate their milk with families looking for donated breastmilk to give their babies. The breastmilk is not screened or pasteurised so the recipient must manage that themselves. Many donors will offer up a detailed lifestyle history but since this milk-sharing outlet is unregulated, the accuracy of the information provided cannot be confirmed. Still, many families choose this option. It is important to make an informed decision if you choose to explore this path, so definitely talk with your health care provider about any potential risks involved.

If you opt out of using donor milk then your other option is formula. Selecting the right formula for your baby is key and sometimes it takes a few tries to find one that meets all your needs and is gentle on your baby's digestive system. We suggest trying out a formula that comes recommended by a midwife. One popular formula is the Holle organic formula from Germany, which comes in either goat's or cow's milk options. A lot of our mama friends love it.

If you don't have enough milk to support what your baby needs, you can still breastfeed, but supplement this with formula. Even tiny doses of breastmilk can be extremely beneficial. Discuss this with your care provider or lactation consultant to figure out the best plan for you and your baby.

No matter what your journey is, the most important thing is that your baby is nourished in the way that works best for your family. Don't judge yourself during this process. You grew a human inside your body and birthed that baby – you are already a rock star!

NAPPIES

Ah, the wonderful world of nappies. Are you going to attempt cloth or are you opting for eco-disposables? Or a bit of both?

Cloth nappies are fantastic for your baby's behind, as they're free from dyes and chemicals. They can also be better for the environment – around 20 billion (regular) disposable nappies end up in landfill every year, and it can take hundreds of years for them to break down. Cloth nappies are also a really great option for people looking to reduce the financial burden of having a babe – on average, from newborn to toilet training, Australian parents will spend $3250 on disposable nappies, compared to $1500 on cloth nappies. The only downside to using cloth is that it can be a lot of work. Once babe has done their business, many choose to use a spray connected to a toilet or shower to spray any of the more solid material off prior to chucking it in to soak or straight the wash. If you're out and about you must carry a waterproof bag to lug the dirty nappies with you (don't do as Teresa has done and forget about them for a couple of days so they stink up your favourite nappy bag!). If you're up for it, we highly recommend owlbaby.com.au for everything to do with cloth nappies. Rachel from Owl Baby is a godsend, and can answer any questions about cloth nappies over the phone. Other amazing cloth nappy brands include GroVia, bumGenius, Bubblebubs and Bamboo Delights.

If you're not going to take the reusable route, eco-disposables are the way to go. Bambo Nature, tooshies by TOM and Ecoriginals are all great options. If you need something with hardcore absorption because your baby is prone to nappy rash, opt for a brand like Pampers and seek out their Pampers Pure range, which is much gentler on both baby and the environment. There are even pioneering companies such as Eenee, which specialises in a compostable nappy made from biodegradable materials, and Botanic Baby, a Melbourne-based service that ensures the Eenee nappies are disposed of correctly. They also offer a service that delivers and launders washable nappies!

Teresa: We did cloth with Bodhi for eight months and he never got nappy rash, not once! Even without using any barrier creams. After that we switched to eco-disposables because we were travelling so much, and bringing cloth nappies on the road proved difficult. Forest wore eco-disposables from the start. We started Poet with disposables but she got a terrible nappy rash, so it was back to cloth – and the rash healed up instantaneously! We're now doing a hybrid approach: predominantly cloth, plus eco-disposables when we are away from home.

WIPES

Babies have verrrrry sensitive skin, especially in their first twelve weeks, so we recommend using cloth wipes with water for at least this early period. Some mamas use reusable strips of soft material as wipes all through their baby's nappy-wearing days; otherwise you can slowly introduce very natural organic disposable wipes. After wiping, make sure you fully dry the bottom area with a soft cloth to ensure no moisture gets caught in the nappy – moisture is the number one cause of nappy rash (more on this below).

BARRIER CREAMS

Barrier creams are a must for little bums as soon as baby starts pooping and peeing up a storm (i.e. as soon as your milk comes in). With each nappy change, you should be putting a barrier cream on to ensure your babe's new skin is protected from irritation. Our favourites are (duh!) Sarah's company Bāeo, which makes an amazing booty balm (100% certified organic) with a beautiful blend of essential oils! Other great brands are Megan Gale's Mindful Life soothing nappy cream, which has a base of zinc in it, as well as MooGoo's Natural Nappy Balm, another fave. There are also companies using organic Australian white clay as a natural powder and a healthy alternative to talc. We love Little Innoscents and Nature's Child Organic Baby Powder.

COMMUNITY QUESTION: WHAT IF MY BABY GETS NAPPY RASH?

This will almost certainly happen at some point, but using barrier creams will help prevent it. If your baby is super sensitive and prone to a red bottom or rash, like Teresa's daughter Poet, use the double whammy: an impenetrable barrier! Smother barrier cream on first, then layer powder on top and pat it in. No poo or pee will ever get through that DEFCON security layer! You can try this pre-emptively as soon as you notice even a slight bit of redness.

If the rash has already appeared, don't panic. There's nothing nappy-free time can't fix! Take the nappy off and air baby's bottom out, keeping it as dry as possible. You can slide an open nappy under their butt to catch any wayward emissions, but make sure you keep checking to see if this has happened, as it will need to be cleaned oh-so-gently, but fast. You don't want any urine or poo irritating an already sore bottom. Sometimes all it takes to remedy a rash is twenty-four hours of nappy-free time.

Going nappy-free for twenty-four hours – including overnight – is a roll-your-sleeves-up hefty commitment, but it *is* a game changer. If you're willing to go there, just put baby down to sleep in a long-sleeved T-shirt with a completely nude lower half. The nappy-free night might mean more waking up for you, as you can't swaddle baby, but believe us when we say it's a great way to heal nappy rash fast. Use the DEFCON method to prevent it from returning.

> **Teresa:** Oh, those no-nappy days – hardcore but oh-so-worth-it. I did forty-eight hours straight with Poet when she was six weeks old, using open nappies during the day and puppy pee pads taped down to the bed underneath her at night time. We were co-sleeping, so I was right by her and could change the pad underneath her whenever it was wet. I had to do this a bunch of times, plus clean her and pat her dry softly. My hubs was out of the country at the time, so it was quite the experience. But it worked. We then switched to cloth, which seemed to help. I discovered the cream/powder combination when she was eight weeks old and her rash never returned – even after re-introducing eco-disposable nappies. I just wish I'd done that barrier method from the start as a preventative!

BATHING

That amazing vernix won't fully absorb into baby's skin until day five or six, so try to hold off on their first sponge bath until then. When you do give your baby her first bath make sure the room is nice and warm and have a towel ready and laid out (you can even pop the towel in the dryer so it will be extra warm and cosy for your baby). You can use a newborn bath or – Sarah's favourite – the kitchen sink. Hold your little one in the water and wash gently.

Some new babies won't be happy being washed in water. This can be alarming for them, and they may not feel secure. For a more peaceful first bath experience, consider hopping in the bath with your baby on your chest, allowing the warm water to roll over them. Don't soak with them for too long, though, as their body temperature can drop pretty quickly. Your baby smells so sweet and they rarely sweat, so you will only need to give them a full bath 2–3 times per week for the first year. Ensure the water is warm, not hot or cool to the touch, and use any soap sparingly, as it can dry your baby's skin out. It's lovely to make a little routine out of bath time: sing some songs, hop in the bath with them, cuddle together. Then wrap them up all cosy in a hooded towel and use your favourite organic baby oil (plugging Bāeo again here!) to do a nice baby massage after bath.

BELLY BUTTON CARE

Your baby's cord stump usually stays attached for around 5–15 days. The cord will dry out and shrink, sometimes it will smell a tad funky, and then it will fall off! When your baby's cord stump is still attached, it's best to fold down the top of the nappy to let the belly button 'breathe' and keep it unobstructed. Many people wait to give baby their first bath until after their cord stump has fallen off, opting for sponge baths until then. If you want to wash babe sooner, wash the stump normally with some soap and warm water, but don't tug or pull at it – it will fall off naturally.

Check with your care provider if you notice any redness around the belly button area, if it's emitting a terrible smell or looks swollen, or if your baby develops a fever or is feeding poorly. These can all be signs of infection.

SOOTHING YOUR BABY

All right folks, listen up, because you're going to want to work out how to soothe your baby pronto – those freshies can belt out a tune or two! Your baby's cries, coos and facial expressions are its only way to communicate with you. Luckily it doesn't take too long to get tuned in to what baby needs, but sometimes you might try all the tricks in the world and still have a crying baby in your arms! That doesn't make you a bad mama, we promise. It can be handy to write a checklist and go down the list whenever you're struggling to soothe your bub.

- First and foremost, put the baby on your breast: are they hungry?
- If that doesn't work, try holding them close and soothing them by rocking, singing or having some skin to skin.
- Still fussing? Check to see if they have a dirty nappy.
- All clean? Perhaps they're tired! Swaddle them, pat them on the bum, lay them down and see if they'll sleep.
- If not, strap your carrier on and walk around, pacing and rocking. More often than not, the warmth of your chest, the sound of your voice and the comfort of being close to mama will calm them down. Often babies will fall asleep in a carrier as it provides them with comfort – and gives you handy hands-free time! Win win. (More on baby wearing below.)
- Remember that yoga ball you used during pregnancy and labour? Save yourself the money on a rocking chair and bounce on a yoga ball while holding your little one. The bouncing simulates the feeling your baby had when you'd walk those five miles a day (ha!) while pregnant.

THE 5 Ss

Dr Harvey Karp, author of *The Happiest Baby on the Block* and co-creator of the SNOO bassinet, has a system of soothing baby that's, well . . . genius!

1. SWADDLE

Swaddling recreates the snug packaging inside the womb and is the cornerstone of calming. It decreases startling and increases sleep. And, wrapped babies respond faster to the other 4 Ss and stay soothed longer because their arms can't wriggle around. To swaddle correctly, wrap arms snug – straight at the side – but let the hips be loose and flexed. Use a large square blanket, but don't overheat, cover your baby's head or allow unravelling. Note: Babies shouldn't be swaddled all day, just during fussing and sleep.

2. SIDE OR STOMACH POSITION

The back is the only safe position for sleeping, but it's the worst position for calming fussiness. This S can be activated by holding a baby on her side, on her stomach or over your shoulder. You'll see your baby mellow in no time.

3. SHUSH

Contrary to myth, babies don't need total silence to sleep. In the womb, the sound of the blood flow is a shush louder than a vacuum cleaner! But, not all white noise is created equal. Hissy fans and ocean sounds often fail because they lack the womb's rumbly quality. The best way to imitate these magic sounds is white noise.

4. SWING

Life in the womb is very jiggly. (Imagine your baby bopping around inside your belly when you jaunt down the stairs!) While slow rocking is fine for keeping quiet babies calm, you need to use fast, tiny motions to soothe a crying infant mid-squawk. To do it, always support the head/neck, keep your motions small; and move no more than a couple of centimetres back and forth. (For the safety of your infant, never, ever shake your baby in anger or frustration.)

5. SUCK

Sucking is 'the icing on the cake' of calming. Many fussy babies relax into a deep tranquility when they suck. Many babies calm easier with a dummy.

TO DUMMY OR NOT TO DUMMY?

This is essentially a take it or leave it situation: babies certainly don't need a dummy but often parents find them useful for soothing their babe. Some studies show that dummy usage may lower the risk of SIDS, while others suggest that introducing a dummy before breastfeeding is well established can interfere with milk supply, negatively impact baby's weight gain, increase the likelihood of ear infections and lead to earlier weaning.[2]

If you want to use a dummy, we believe it's good to do so sparingly, and to only offer it to your baby between feeds when you're sure they aren't hungry – this will ensure the dummy doesn't take the place of a feed. Wait until your baby is at least six weeks old and breastfeeding is well established before introducing a dummy. Using a dummy can be a wonderful way to soothe baby, but it can later turn into a nightmare when you're trying to convince your three-year-old to give the dummy away to 'the dummy fairy'!

Sarah: Both of my kids used dummies to calm their gassy tummies and soothe their desire to suckle at the breast non-stop, but they decided they were all done with them by around ten months old.

Teresa: I never used a dummy with Bodhi and Forest because I didn't feel the need to – they were happy sucking on fingers (mine or theirs!) and finding their own way to self-soothe. Bodhi and Forest simply grew out of their high sucking needs, but Poet is my 'suckiest' baby, sucking her thumb all the time. We ended up buying a dummy to calm her crying in the car, and of course that same dummy made its way into my trailer at work. Our babysitter uses it to help get Poet down to sleep. As soon as I'm finished this job, in the bin it goes! But for now it's a nice comfort for her.

BABY WEARING

We are major advocates of wearing our babies around the house, on nature walks, while doing the shopping and just about any place we go. It's good for you, good for the baby and it makes life easier: you suddenly have your hands free! Dr William Sears, a paediatrician, author of many parenting books and an expert on attachment theory, explains the benefits:

Baby wearing is a great way to continue to bond with your baby. By carrying your baby in a wrap or sling, you are able to hear every sound. Babies that are carried in this manner tend to nurse more which also helps maintain mom's milk supply. As you take your baby out and about, the sound of your heartbeat and warmth of your body are soothing. Being that close also allows baby to have more interaction and have shown to develop faster in some areas because of watching your behavior.

We've tried out lots of different types of carriers; here's a lowdown of our favourites. Note that there can be risks from incorrect babywearing so make sure you follow directions, are using your carrier properly and have help when you are learning how to babywear.[3]

STRUCTURED CARRIERS

Structured carriers are great because they're so easy to use. Our partners love wearing our babes in them too. BabyBjörn's ONE is an amazing carrier with easy-to-use clips for getting baby in and out efficiently on your own (essential for when you're flying solo). Ergo is a favourite in the natural mama community – they now offer the Ergo 360 for babes who love to look around while being carried. Other great brands are Beco, Tula and Pognae. Do a deep dive, chat to some other baby-wearing mamas, try the carriers out in the stores and get the right one for you.

Check out Gumtree for cost-efficient options – they have great lightly worn second-hand carriers on the regular.

WRAPS

While snuggly, beautifully patterned, cosy wraps are absolutely delightful, it does take skill to do a good wrap, as there's a lot of material to wrangle. There are many tutorials on how to wrap the right way, and tonnes of different techniques for how to carry your baby depending on their age, but once you get the hang of them people tend to love them. Sometimes babies who are prone to overheating struggle with a wrap, but trying one of the more lightweight brands (we like Solly Baby) could help address this issue.

RING SLINGS

These are a great go-to for ease and style – you get the benefits of the wrap, without having to perfect the tie. Ring Slings allow air flow to reach the baby – this is particularly helpful in summer, or if (like Teresa) you have a baby who runs really hot. It takes a little effort to get the right fit, but once it clicks in it's wonderful. Our favourite brands are Little Frog, Girasol, LÍLLÉbaby and Fidella.

T-SHIRT CARRIERS

Essentially this is just a T-shirt with a pocket in the front for baby to slide into. It's a very cool invention, but depending on the size of your baby, a T-shirt carrier is only really practical for the first six weeks or so, otherwise baby gets too squirmy and it's hard to mould the shape to them properly (unlike a wrap).

Do try out all the different types of carriers to find your favourite.

Don't worry if you're as crap at baby wrapping as Teresa is.

Don't eat or drink hot stuff when wearing your baby.

Do take photos of all the cold food you drop on your sleeping child's head.

Don't wear a jumpsuit or playsuit while babywearing as you will not be able to go to the toilet.

Do wear baby cautiously near any sharp objects (duh).

Don't drink and wear baby (double duh).

Do ensure baby is close enough to kiss on the top of the head.

Don't let go of baby until you're absolutely confident that they are secure and safe.

Do take a break if your back is hurting or you simply need a rest (or a poo).

Don't bend at the waist while wearing baby; bend using your knees instead.

Do ask for help if you're worried about positioning.

Don't feel guilty if you've had enough and want to just whip out the pram!

SLEEEEEEP

You know that saying, 'Slept like a baby'? It must have been inspired by those rare freshies who actually *do* sleep well for long periods! At about 6–8 weeks old your baby's naps will get a lot shorter, and they'll suddenly show greater sensitivity to noise. You'll be tiptoeing around them, trying not to make a sound when PING: their big wide eyes will spring open (and you know that brief moment to yourself is over!). We are all about extending sleep and ensuring that everyone is getting as much rest as possible. Here are some tips from experts in this area, as well as our own combined years of trying to get multiple young babies off to sleep.

SLEEPING LOCATIONS

Where will your baby sleep? In a cot, co-sleeper, Moses basket, SNOO, baby lounger, or on a Montessori mattress? There are many schools of thought and many things to consider when making this decision. Sleep safety experts recommend that babies share your room for the first 6–12 months, and that room-sharing with your baby lowers the risk of SUDI (sudden unexpected death in infancy).[4]

We both kept our children in our room for at least the first two years. Our sleeping arrangements varied from co-sleeping (always sticking to the safe co-sleeping guidelines mentioned below), using the DockATot (a lounging/sleeping dock for babies and toddlers), using a co-sleeping side-car crib and using Dr Harvey Karp's SNOO, which is designed to create a womb-like environment for your baby with soothing white noise and movement to aid sleep. (Disclaimer: the SNOO is very pricey, so maybe you could add it to your baby shower list as a communal gift, or, as Teresa does, get one between friends and share it around!) Once our babies were over two years old, we both used a Montessori-style sleeping set-up, with a mattress on the floor in our bedroom so our kids started the night in their own bed nearby but came into ours halfway through. Each bub is different, and so too are your needs.

Some light-sleeping mamas can't sleep if their baby is in their room making all those little snuffling noises during their sleep. We suggest using a sound machine and/or earplugs if you have a noisy sleeper. Baby's cries will wake you even with earplugs in, it'll just dull out some of the louder breathing and noises, allowing you to get more rest. Just find a sound machine, some amazing silicon earplugs or a great soothing song to sleep to (*Chanting the Sacred Mantra Om: Music for Deep Meditation* is the go-to night-time sound machine in Teresa's household).

Babies crave closeness and putting them in their own room to sleep is less safe, according to experts. It can also create nighttime separation anxiety and cause more night wakings. Having to get up and out of bed, turn the light on, walk into the nursery and change/nurse the baby will interrupt mama's sleep more abruptly, too. We believe room sharing for the first few months is easier for the parents, promotes better-quality sleep and is more harmonious for all. Naturally there are always exceptions to the rule – some babies do way better having their own space. After around four months some parents start to transition their little ones to a crib, while others continue to room share. Find what works best for your baby and your family.

CREATE A WOMB-LIKE ENVIRONMENT

Babies are fresh out of the womb and still seeking the creature comforts of that environment. Swaddling them for their naps can help provide this. Babies have the 'Morro' reflex, which means they throw their arms out in surprise when they're being put down or even in the middle of a dream. Often this motion wakes them up or startles them. Swaddling restricts that reflex, meaning babies can sleep with less chance of being awoken by sudden changes in their environment, such as lights, noises or altitude changes (e.g. being put down). The majority of babies LOVE a swaddle and will sleep much better all swaddled up, but some don't like it at all. Read your baby's cues; you'll soon know if you've got a happy swaddler.

Another great way to mimic the womb is to keep babe's sleeping area nice and dark with blackout curtains, and add a sound machine. When your baby was bouncing around happily in the womb they were rocking out to the anthem of your heartbeat, organs pumping, blood whooshing. This means that they're used to napping in a darkened, white noise-filled space, so recreating that environment can be very soothing. The four-stage combo of nursing, swaddling, dark room and white noise has helped many women around the world get their babies to sleep!

We are co-sleeping mothers but we are hyper-aware of what makes a co-sleeping arrangement dangerous and how to co-sleep safely with our babies. Many studies suggest that a large number of parents will end up sleeping with their baby for part of the night, though many won't admit to it.[5] Why the secrecy and the controversy? Well, co-sleeping is met with very mixed opinions.

Factors that can make co-sleeping dangerous include smoking, alcohol, drug use, overcrowded beds, low infant birth weight, prone sleep positions and hazardous sleeping surfaces. Many studies since then have concluded that *safe* co-sleeping practices do not increase the risk to infants.

Professor James McKenna, leading mother–baby behavioural sleep specialist, explains the benefits of co-sleeping: 'In Japan where co-sleeping and breastfeeding (in the absence of maternal smoking) is the cultural norm, rates of the sudden infant death syndrome are the lowest in the world. For breastfeeding mothers, bedsharing makes breastfeeding much easier to manage and practically doubles the amount of breastfeeding sessions while permitting both mothers and infants to spend more time asleep. The increased exposure to mother's antibodies which comes with more frequent nighttime breastfeeding can potentially, per any given infant, reduce infant illness.'[6]

There are some very strict guidelines around co-sleeping, which we follow diligently. While we advocate for co-sleeping and bedsharing, it must *always* be done in a responsible, deliberate and informed way. Professor McKenna highlights that while co-sleeping is supported by many credible sources and institutions (including La Leche League International, UNICEF and the World Health Organization), it's important to be aware of the guidelines. A bed should never be shared between a newborn and other siblings. Co-sleeping adults must not be inebriated or overly exhausted, as this can hamper their awareness of their newborn. Dr McKenna's studies have highlighted that breastfeeding mothers and infants may have a heightened awareness of each other while sleeping, and he suggests that bottlefeeding infants should sleep in a co-sleeper alongside the parents, but not in the same bed.

Professor McKenna summarises the key elements that make up a safe co-sleeping environment in his Safe Co-sleeping Guidelines.[7] These include:

- Regardless of where the infant sleeps, they should be on their back on a firm, clean surface, under lightweight covering but with their head uncovered. There should be no secondhand smoke in the environment.
- Bottlefeeding babies should always sleep alongside the mother on a separate surface rather than in the bed.
- Both parents should agree on the co-sleeping arrangement, be aware that the baby is present and take equal responsibility for him or her.
- Babies younger than a year old should not sleep with older children/siblings.
- Co-sleeping on the same surface must not occur if either parent is intoxicated, has taken drugs, sedatives or medication, or is otherwise unable to rouse themselves from sleep.
- Mothers with long hair should tie it up to prevent entanglement around the baby's neck (tragically, this is possible).
- Parents who are extremely obese or who may have difficulty feeling exactly where or how close their infant is in relation to their own body, may wish to have the infant sleep alongside but on a different surface, such as a co-sleeper attachment.

Co-sleeping and/or room sharing isn't for everyone, but we have both found that it offers multiple advantages, the most fruitful one being MORE SLEEP. We both tried putting our first babies down in their own rooms for the night, but it was exhausting getting up to feed/change our babies multiple times per night. Make the decision that's right for your family – happy parents make better parents. You can use all the same methods to soothe, calm and create a womb-like environment for your baby in their own room, too, if that feels more practical for you.

THE CRY IT OUT METHOD

The Cry It Out (CIO) method was established in 1913, although some suggest that its true origins stemmed from Emmett Holt's 1894 book, *The Care and Feeding of Children*. The CIO method has since been closely linked to paediatrician Dr Richard Ferber, who supports the notion that by letting babies cry themselves to sleep you teach them how to self-soothe. The baby is allowed to cry without being comforted for increasingly long periods of time until they learn that their cries will go unnoticed. (This is different from 'controlled comforting', which allows up to 10 minutes of crying in infants over 6 months.) CIO is a subject of much debate, so we wanted to share our take on it.

Babies cry for all sorts of reasons: perhaps they've got themselves in an awkward position, maybe they're scared, hungry, ill, have a dirty nappy, or they're just feeling vulnerable. Crying is a baby's only way to communicate, and they do so in the hope that someone will come to their aid. Studies of human infants confirm that prolonged crying is physiologically stressful and increases babies' cortisol levels, heart rate and energy expenditure.[8]

We sought the input of award-winning psychologist and neuroscience researcher Dr Darcia Narvaez, professor of psychology at the University of Notre Dame and host of EvolvedNest.org, who says:

Humans are highly immature at birth and their social experience actually sculpts their neurobiology – systems such as the stress response, oxytocin and serotonin, all of which are related to intelligences of various kinds. Because babies are rapidly developing hundreds of systems, nearly everything babies experience can become engraved in their bodies and brains.

Caregivers who habitually respond to the needs of the baby *before* the baby gets distressed (that means before they cry, which is a late signal of needs) are more likely to have children who are both cooperative and independent than the opposite.

So when people discuss or prescribe 'crying it out' sleep training (CIO), I get alarmed. It is not advised. When CIO is used in the first couple of years of life it can undermine a child's lifelong attachment security and sense of trust – and these influence how well the individual self-regulates and gets along with others. Distressing a child routinely in early life has particular negative effects that may only show up later as anxiety, depression, low empathy or cruelty.

There are many schools of thought surrounding CIO. Our personal position is that it doesn't feel good to dull our natural instincts as a parent; we want to comfort our children when they need us. We both take the approach of 'meeting the need when the need arises'. If you feel the need to try a more structured sleep regimen with your baby, there are also other, gentler techniques that don't mean leaving your baby to cry it out for prolonged periods.

EARLY DEVELOPMENT

In the fourth trimester your baby is so new to the world that their main job is feeling secure, safe and comfortable in this entirely undiscovered environment. They are getting to know 'their people', and they'll respond well to gentle touch, soothing voices and love. You cannot spoil a child this young: all they need and crave is your touch, connection and loving warmth. It's what literally makes them thrive.

Right from the start we suggest reading, singing and talking to them – bring your face 15–30 centimetres away from theirs, which is about as far as they can see, and make different expressions. You'll notice your baby fixating on you and enjoying your attention. As the weeks go by and their colour vision develops, you can introduce brightly coloured toys to them (they won't be able to see pastel palettes well yet). Do not underestimate the importance of connecting with your babe, looking them in the eye and showing them that they have your focus. This all helps develop a secure attachment.

Day by day you'll start to see your baby discover new things about their body. Supervised 'tummy time' – laying them on their tummy – will help them build their strength and begin developing the skills needed to crawl and walk. They'll be moving their arms around (it's kinda cute when they don't have control and whack themselves in the face!), lifting their legs up and gaining strength in their neck during this period. Aim for 1–2 minutes of supervised tummy time per day when they're newborns, gradually increasing to about 20–30 minutes per day. Their neck will need to be supported when you hold them until well into their fourth month. Each baby develops at a different rate, but from 5–8 weeks you can expect your baby to respond to your voice with eye contact, and to start cooing and reaching for objects. Between 6 and 12 weeks they'll show you the very first hints of real smiles, followed by squeals and giggles. It feels incredible when your baby looks you in the eyes and responds to you by smiling or laughing. Think of this as their little thank you for all those nappy changes and bleary-eyed nights!

We loved using and referencing the *Wonder Weeks* app and book. This is a really fun way to identify and follow the new discoveries your baby will experience each week. It will also show you what to look out for and how to help your baby, guiding you through both the sunny and the stormy times, when your baby may be fussier, hungrier, more wakeful or needing more cuddles. The app gives you some great tips on how to help baby, tells you what to expect and also reassures you that everything is normal in the world when your six-hours-a-night sleeper suddenly becomes a 'two hours then wants to play' non-sleeper!

SCHEDULES

Some folks take comfort in the organisation that comes with following a schedule – so if it works for you, chart away, Mama! When it comes to scheduling we are both of the 'meet the needs when they arise' philosophy. In line with our Zen approach to parenting, we find letting baby lead the way and taking cues directly from them works best for our families.

This means that when it comes to travel or being out and about, our kids are very adaptable. We have never had to worry about rushing home for naps or feeds and having to schedule our days around our baby's routine. Our little ones can (and do!) take naps in all kinds of places: in our arms, at the restaurant booth, in a pram, car seat, plane, carrier, friend's couch or even during the new *The Lion King* (even they know the original was better!). After a few weeks, you'll begin seeing a loose pattern form in their natural routine, anyway. We'll get into the ins and outs of a kid-filled lifestyle a bit more in the next chapter.

The first twelve weeks of your baby's life are full of ALL THE FEELS. You'll be exhausted one minute, joyful the next. And you'll power through it like the warrior you are, making choices every day, finessing and finding your flow. Your journey will be unique, and you'll see just how quickly your newborn is changing before your eyes. Sob!

ZEN NOTES

- Establishing breastfeeding ain't no walk in the park for most. You'll need support.

- Your baby might flip nights and days (oh the joys!). This is normal. Try to recreate a womb-like environment for longer night-time sleep.

- Follow your trusty checklist for soothing and comforting an upset baby.

- Less is more – stuff, that is, especially for the newborn stage. And remember, you can get most things secondhand (saving some money while you're at it).

- For further savings, go old-school and try cloth nappies and reusable wipes.

- You don't have to be a wrap master to wear your baby (just don't wear a playsuit!).

- You're doing a great job, Mama, even when you look or feel like a (not-always) hot mess.

BABYHOOD & BEYOND

EIGHT

Wherever you see happy, peaceful individuals; wherever you see children endowed with noble qualities and good dispositions; wherever you see men who have immense strength when faced with failure and adverse situations; wherever you see people who possess a great measure of understanding, sympathy, love, and compassion towards the suffering, and who give of themselves to others – you will usually find a great mother who has inspired them to become what they are.

Mothers are the ones who are most able to sow the seeds of love, universal kinship, and patience in the minds of human beings.

– AMMA, SRI MATA AMRITANANDAMAYI DEVI FROM HER ADDRESS 'THE AWAKENING OF UNIVERSAL MOTHERHOOD' DELIVERED ON THE OCCASION OF A GLOBAL PEACE INITIATIVE OF WOMEN RELIGIOUS & SPIRITUAL LEADERS, PALAIS DES NATIONS, GENEVA, 7 OCTOBER 2002

By the end of the fourth trimester you may have found your flow with your little one. Of course, this is just the beginning of your lives together. So many more milestones and precious moments await – more than we could ever cover in this book!

In this final chapter, we'll briefly discuss a bunch of approaches we take within our own families regarding self-care, cultivating rewarding relationships, striving for a healthy work/life balance, instinctual parenting, utilising conscious communication with our children, practising gentle discipline techniques and raising eco-minded, global citizens. We hope this provides a bit of insight into our broader parenting philosophy.

BEING ZEN(ISH) PARENTS

What kind of parent do you want to be? This is a big question to ask yourself. If you take a moment to think about it, words such as patient, encouraging, fun, supportive, nurturing and gentle might spring to mind. The truth is, you'll never really know what kind of parent you'll be until you're walking that path with your kids, but it's worth putting some thought into it before they arrive. We're the foundation of the kids we raise, so let's start with a good look at ourselves!

KNOW YOURSELF AND DO THE WORK

Raising children is complex and nuanced. There is no one right way; we are all figuring it out as we go along. A universal truth, though, is that in order to be the best we can be for our children, we need to look at our own patterns of behaviour and work on ourselves. Often this self-work runs parallel to raising our children – though if we are lucky, it starts *before* we have kids – but it is work that's never-ending. The closer we look at our own emotions and behaviours, the better equipped we will be to parent with loving awareness.

Children can be powerful triggers. All sorts of things might come up on our parenting journey. We may be carrying unresolved angst, fear, resentment and disappointment towards our own caregivers, and these emotions can rear their ugly heads when we become parents. Our own childhood experiences make up the fabric of who we are, and these pieces of ourselves can prove to be both confronting and surprising. It's a nice practice when you're pregnant or a new mama to reflect back on (and even journal) your early memories. Observe your thoughts. How do you feel about your relationship with your own parents? If any animosity is present, think about the steps you can take towards healing those wounds.

We have to separate what is about us and what is actually about our children or parents. This can be challenging, as the waters tend to get muddied easily. As parents, we need to conduct careful self-analysis to identify and address the issues that our child is triggering within us, causing us to react. Our advice? Sit in anything that comes up, observe it, work through it and then you can move forwards.

Taking the time to connect with ourselves is an essential part of this. Aside from practising self-love and healing old wounds, we also need to ensure we have a well of tools deep enough that, no matter how painful our past hurts are, we have the methods to navigate them. If we fail to do the work, our kids can feel unfairly the brunt of it. For the two of us, meditation, self-reflection, journalling, therapy, affirmations and reading the wisdom of great spiritual teachers have all aided us on our paths to be our best selves. (We love the writings of Eckhart Tolle and Alan Watts, among others.) Find what resonates with you and take steps towards understanding yourself better; this can only guide you towards a more harmonious family dynamic.

CREATING BALANCE

A happy parent is a better parent. Think of yourself as the trunk of a large oak tree, with branches peeling off, weaving and twisting high into the sky, held strong by the trunk. These branches are the aspects of your life that mean the most to you: children, work, your partner, friends, family, passions, spirituality, whatever else they may be. Without a strong trunk to support them, the branches can't grow outwards.

Tending to you, the trunk, is of the utmost importance. To have nourishing and meaningful relationships, you must first have a loving and connected relationship to your *self*. You can't pour from an empty cup, as they say. So, how can you show up for yourself today? How can you tend to your emotional, physical and mental needs? How can you honour yourself? How can you show gratitude to yourself? How can you nurture the little child within you? We must work on cultivating love, acceptance and kindness towards ourselves as an everyday practice. Look at the way your children love you, their untainted vision of who you are: can you find that same love for yourself? From this place, the possibilities are boundless and you can be all you wish to be as a mother, sister, partner, friend, neighbour and citizen of this world.

You might be wondering how we can focus on self yet also tend to the needs of our family, all while existing within societal constructs. We have jobs to fulfil, domestic duties to tend to, social events, school runs, bills to pay, etc. The grunt work is a time suck, and we typically put ourselves at the very bottom of our to-do lists, meaning we often ignore our own wishes. It's helpful to get organised: look at your week, find those things that don't fall within your most valued list and say no to them. Prioritise, and keep true to your daily self-care non-negotiables!

INVESTING IN OUR RELATIONSHIPS

Relationships can be hard enough already, but throw some little whipper snappers into the mix and suddenly it can feel like your relationship has been hit with a sledgehammer! Studies show that having children often leads to overall marriage dissatisfaction.[1] Yowzers! So, what do we do with that information? We take measures to kid-proof our partnerships!

You are teammates, taking on some of life's most challenging and tedious work. Parenting gives the most incredible rewards and offers all the love you could imagine, but it isn't for the faint-hearted. There'll be days when you'll collapse into bed thinking 'Oh god, I'm back at it again tomorrow', or moments when you're so damn touched out that when your honey gives you *that* look, you just want to hide under the covers!

Teresa: When Mark and I first got together we read the book *The 5 Love Languages* by Dr Gary Chapman to establish what our love languages are. Mark's are physical touch and quality time, whereas mine are quality time and acts of service (The washing and the dishes have been done, honey! Oh, and how 'bout a nice massage to top it all off!). After the kids were born I felt touched out, and any spare time I had I wanted to use for a nap or taking a bath. Mark wasn't feeling like his needs were being met by me, whereas I felt like all I was doing was meeting everyone else's needs. What really worked for us was a couple of sessions with a marriage therapist (shout-out to Dr Stan Tatkin!). We also put a ban on devices for ourselves from 8.30 to 10.30 p.m. We spent that time connecting with each other; doing a meditation together, reading a book out loud to each other, listening to a podcast or working on our next baby!! (Oh, the irony.)

Sometimes all we really need in our romantic relationships is acknowledgement. We are human beings and we love to receive praise. It's natural! So our advice is just to be kind to each other. What does your partner need in this moment? What is their way? What is their love language? Do they crave affection? Quality time? A kind gesture? Sometimes it's as little as giving them a hand squeeze or getting someone over to babysit so you can have an uninterrupted evening indulging in adult conversation (which will probably end up being about the kids!). It might be as simple as taking the time to look at your partner and say, 'Thank you so much for being so present with the kids today; I know how much it meant to them. You're an amazing father', or, 'Darling, you're so loving and giving as a mother, our children are so lucky to have you in their lives.' Finding even the smallest moments to pat each other on the back can reinforce your bond and provide positive reassurance.

At the end of a crazy day with the kids, fall into bed together, ban the devices and put the work aside: it can wait. Be with each other, have a moment of connection. Check in. How are you doing? Look into each other's eyes, remember why you fell in love and then giggle at the madness of it all. The two of you are the foundation of this family, so treat your partnership with the love and care it deserves.

Life with a child is guaranteed to change your partnership. To protect your relationship and sense of self, it's best to prepare now, before the baby arrives. Take some time during pregnancy to imagine how your life may be different with a baby, and how your current relationships may transform in postpartum life.

Here are what I call the Three Primary Postpartum Pitfalls – the things that can create tension in relationships.

1. Letting the baby run the show. It is normal to become overly focused on your new baby. However, the secret to a happy relationship with children is to put your relationship with your partner first. This creates a sense of safety and security, allowing your children to flourish. So have fun! It is the closeness and bond between partners that nurtures our little ones.

2. Keeping score. A true team is a situation in which when you have a free hand, you jump in to help. It is not keeping score. Findings have shown that the best aphrodisiac is the person who comes home and just pitches in wherever they can.

3. Losing sight of having fun. Often, we get lost in the drudgery of things that have to get done. Life becomes all business, all the time, and partners find themselves feeling unhappy, lost and unfulfilled. As new parents, we need to make it a priority to talk, date and have fun . . . sex anyone? Every week should include a date for emotional connection and moments of physical connection. By keeping your relationship strong, you are giving your children the environment they need to thrive.

All of these preparations will feed your relationship, making your partnership stronger. This ensures that your home is still filled with friendship, love and devotion. Change can be scary and anxiety-producing, but be open to the thoughts and emotions that will present themselves to you. There's no need to judge them or yourself; just be aware of their presence and embrace the ups and downs. It's an exciting time of life for both of you.

— DR ALYSSA BERLIN, PSYD

WORKING WHILE HAVING KIDS

What a parent's working life looks like really depends on the job you have. In some countries, parental leave stretches up to a year or two postpartum, whereas in others, mums are expected back at work only weeks after their little one is born, and for dads it can be a matter of days. If you love your job and have a plan in place for what happens when your parental leave is up then you are one of the lucky ones.

Moving away from the standard arrangement of taking leave from a full-time or part-time job, hundreds of thousands of Aussie mums are starting their own businesses. According to Mums & Co, an Australian-based business collective, 32 per cent of mums start a business while on parental leave. In their survey of 852 mums, 57 per cent said the motivation was flexible hours and location, 54 per cent said it was empowerment to do things the way they want to, and 44 per cent said they started a business because of a passion for what they are doing. The best bit is that 77 per cent of survey respondents said they feel happier as a result of building their own business. [2]

We both have jobs that allow us to bring our children with us, but they still go to school and have playdates and after-school activities. We need the help of a grandparent, partner or nanny while we are actually working, but for the most part our jobs are short-term, with months off in between, which gives us the chance to be both stay-at-home mums and working mums. We know this is a privilege, and it's one we are insanely grateful for.

Sarah: When you become a mum, many things happen inside your body. For me, it was as if my brain hyper-focused on my passions and creativity, and a desire to work on those things took over.

When we started having babies, the drive to work on the things we were passionate about grew even stronger. This gave us more perspective on what mattered most to us and the ways we wanted to contribute to the world. That was when Yourzenmama.com was born: we launched the community after having our first babies and while pregnant with our second. We longed for a community to connect with that shared our values and that we could learn from, while also allowing us the space to share, grow and explore our own philosophies.

Alongside working on Your Zen Mama we both also launched other brands, baeo.com (Sarah) and lovewell.earth (Teresa). These are companies born from the shared mission of giving families cleaner, organic, plant-based and eco-friendly options when it comes to the products they use and the nutrition that goes into their bodies. Between the businesses, raising our children and filming (among our other pursuits – ahem, this book!), our schedules get very intense. Our biggest piece of advice is to get help! This may mean you have an intern for a few weeks to carry some of your business workload, hire a nanny (Sar couldn't do it without her beloved Sonya), have your parents step in to help out (shout-out to Teresa's two mums, Paula and Kaaren!) or delegate jobs to your partner. There have been many late nights when we've stayed up to finish a chapter, prep vlogs for the site, prep social or marketing for our companies or catch up on everything else. It does sometimes feel like a lot, but we love it and as long as we can do it and still be present with our families, we will keep figuring out new ways to make it work. Just don't try and be super mum boss juggling it all, because something will inevitably suffer. If that thing ends up being your sanity, then none of it will work!

Teresa: I am a chronic over-committer and launching Lovewell (with my business partner Chrissy) as I was pregnant with my third baby and six months out from embarking on a gruelling 65+ hour shooting schedule for my TV show was, as Mark says, 'in true Tez style'. And boy, was it both crazy-making and rewarding. My motivation for starting Lovewell was wanting to create a conscious-minded business that gave me the freedom to choose my hours and, most importantly, as a means to take on fewer acting gigs so I could have even longer full-time stay-at-home mum periods. We've had a first year that we never expected – we sold out our first two runs, which caught us out without stock for a month (not ideal!). We've learnt so much, and made so many mistakes, but we've grown from them all. It's really important to know your limitations. I know I'm spread too thin when I'm filming, and the business suffers without us hiring someone to hold up my end of the responsibilities.

So what does this work life look like in terms of spending time with kids? Our goal is probably similar to most: finding a way to be home and be present with our children while also working on the things that we love. It's not easy, and what often comes with doing any job while raising kids is the feeling of 'mum guilt'. We battle it often and try to find balance in the midst of work, pick-ups, drop-offs, playdates, family dinners and self-care. It takes time and patience to finesse your flow as a working mama. Just remind yourself of the gift you're giving your children by showing them how colourful your life is. Let your children visit you at your work and see you immersed in your job so they get a better sense of what 'work' looks like.

Sarah: My mum worked a full-time job when we were growing up. She did long hours and was very tired at the end of the day. Our time together as a family was around the dinner table – my dad cooked dinner and it was piping hot and ready to go when my mum walked in the door. Looking back on my childhood, this was something I valued so deeply because we got time to sit down with our mum and talk about our day while enjoying the amazing food my dad prepared. This beautiful and simple tradition became normal life for me (and was the same for my husband) and we carry it on in our own family, with home-cooked meals eaten together almost every night.

The modern-day worker is expected to be 'on' around the clock; email, text messaging and mobile phones have created the expectation of immediate responses at all hours. This doesn't allow much time in the 'unplugged' space. We've found that the most effective way to sustain any balance is to have boundaries and guidelines in place. We've come across many great suggestions from books we've read, such as *The Secrets of Happy Families* by Bruce Feiler, *Permission to Parent* by Robin Berman and *Raising Lions* by Joe Newman. From these books, from friends, from our own childhoods and from our mentors we've pulled together the following guidelines that we use as a means of bringing some structure to our unconventional schedules.

- We start the day every morning with breakfast together (we know it's hard to sit and have breakfast during the rush to get ready, but this is a nice way to connect before the busy day begins).
- After school we go home and have a snack, play together, work on an art project, play a board game or do homework.
- While we cook dinner, our kids play or help out in the kitchen.
- We have family dinner together every night (or as often as possible). This allows time to discuss our days and check in with questions that will provoke more than a one-word answer, such as 'Did anyone get in trouble today?', 'Who did you sit next to at lunch?' or 'Was there a new letter you learned today?'

We maintain a bathtime/bedtime routine. Remember that bathtime routine you started when your little one was a baby? This can continue in its own way for many years. As your little one becomes more independent they may want to take a shower or bath on their own, but you can still help with PJs, reading, singing songs before bed and generally enjoying some dedicated unplugged time for your children to connect with you.

Sarah: We have a ritual in our family: when we get to the end of the week, we ask each other (my husband and I included) what was the peach and what was the pit of the week. This encourages our little ones to discuss the highs and the lows, so we can help them figure out if there is a way to handle any situation differently, or check in if something is bothering them. We do this at the end of trips too, which provokes some interesting conversation about everyone's perspective on a vacation and what they value the most.

OUR CONNECTIONS WITH OUR KIDS

Before we had kids, we had a preconceived idea of what it meant to be 'connected' to our children. We believed this to be as simple as being a friend to them, spending quality time, having an open dialogue with them, etc. All of these things are important, but as our parenting journey has unfolded we've stumbled across so many other pearls of wisdom. Here are our favourites.

ATTACHMENTS AND INSTINCTS

Children crave closeness, attachment, love, touch, affection and nurturing (among other things, of course!). A secure attachment with our children is vital. Attachment theory was first discussed by the psychoanalyst John Bowlby, who studied the emotional effects of infant/parent separation. There are four attachment styles: secure attachment, ambivalent-insecure attachment, avoidant-insecure attachment and disorganised-insecure attachment. There's no doubt we all want our children to enjoy secure attachment. But how do we get there?

When we, as their caregivers, meet our child's needs in a loving and attentive way, we set them up for feeling secure in the world because they know that we are there to catch them when they fall. As they grow, they'll organically learn how to land without always needing us to steady them. Our kids' childhood experiences and the attachments they form shape the person they'll become, greatly informing how they are in the world and how they'll be in their relationships with others.

It's our strong belief that we *should* be their emotional regulators until they've learned their own tools for effective self-regulation. This is why we're wary of enforcing strict schedules with our babies. It is why we choose not to ignore our instincts to tend to our children's cries. It is why we don't stop nursing them to sleep despite being told 'You'll create bad habits', and why we feel that cuddling them, sharing our sleep space or breastfeeding them beyond the first year doesn't mean we're spoiling or coddling them.

We believe that having an overly dogmatic and regimented approach to the care of one's baby curbs their inherent natural instincts and dampens our own maternal intuition. Instead, we enjoy working collaboratively with our children to meet their needs, learning along the way what is working and what is not. Play detective with your baby, listen to them and look for visual cues, and you'll soon be in a great responsive rhythm with your child.

In 1975 Jean Liedloff wrote a book called *The Continuum Concept*, which is beloved by us and gazillions of other natural-leaning folks. Jean spent several years with the Yequana and Sanema tribes of South America and took note of how well adjusted, independent, attuned and connected the children in these communities were. Jean notes how the mothers of these tribal communities kept their babies in carriers and continued about their day. They didn't make their babies the centre of their universe, they just got on with their lives and folded their babies into their routine. These little ones were immersed in the normal life of adults and society, thus absorbing the outside world, learning important things about the workings of it all. This nurtures attachment while teaching your children that they are a piece of the puzzle, not THE piece of the puzzle, softening any entitlement that can arise.

INDIVIDUALITY AND RESPECT

Parenting is an ever-evolving process and you will undoubtedly learn more about your child and their needs as you go along. Let this inform you on how best to meet their needs. It may sound obvious, but our children are unique individuals – they're not extensions of ourselves. Each child is completely different.

We believe in respecting and honouring our kids as their own people. Our 'style', as it were, grew from keeping this in the forefront of our minds. How do we nourish our relationships with our children? We provide guidance, love and support, while also allowing them to unfold into who they intrinsically are.

Babies, toddlers and children have an innate competency, and we like to be respectful of their independence and abilities, regardless of how young they are. Even as newborns you can start to implement this idea by broadcasting as you do things for them, e.g. 'I'm going to change your nappy', or if they're crying, 'I see you're upset, I'm going to pick you up'. This may feel weird at first, but communicating with them clearly and consciously from a young age is about respecting their space and including them in your choices. It also sets up a pattern of transparency with your child, and establishes a trusting bond.

Nature has a perfect plan. Your child is doing things at their own organic pace without the need to prompt, teach or direct them. Famed child educator and founder of RIE parenting (short for Resources for Infant Educarers), Magda

Gerber, promotes the idea of observing your child more and doing less for them. For example, let them work out how to reach the toy on the floor rather than moving it closer to them. Don't do for them what they might be capable of doing for themselves. Leaving them to rely upon their own tenacity reaffirms the notion that they have wondrous abilities to problem solve, even from a very young age.

Our children each have their own visions of the world around them, and if left to self-direct their own play, they start to embrace their unique way in the world. Tackling their own hurdles (within reason) and following their passions without a parent always stepping in instils confidence in them, and gives them a sense of accomplishment and an understanding of their inherent efficiency.

LANGUAGE

Communication is key when it comes to parenting. Being mindful with our words is a beautiful way of ensuring that our children feel heard and seen. Taking the time to observe our habits of speech is a great exercise in slowing down and speaking with tenderness. Let language be your ally.

Let's say your child takes a tumble and starts to cry. Instead of immediately saying, 'You're all right, up you get!' pause for a moment. Your child doesn't actually feel all right, do they? Instead of *telling them* how they are, take the time to validate their feelings. Try saying, 'Oh, I saw that you fell: that must've hurt!' before comforting them.

Or maybe your three-year-old is having a right old tanty at the shops. Rather than yelling at them, try to get down on their level and look them in the eyes. Meet them with empathy. You might say, 'I see you're having a really hard time. You seem angry.' You might notice your child calming down quicker and searching your face to see how you're reacting.

We want to embrace and accept all that our children throw at us emotionally, to create a safe space where they can experience all their big feelings without any rejection or shame. We want to show them that our love is unconditional. Fluctuating and passionate emotions are normal for children, and they should be able to express them all freely. It can be somewhat scary and overwhelming to be a little person with such large emotions. In these moments, ask yourself how you can empathise with your child. Let them know you're here for them. Sit with them and take some deep breaths together, maybe offer your arms as a resting place. Your reassuring energy will calm them.

If we can show them the tools to self-regulate, our kids will start to see that it's possible for them to talk through their feelings rather than just impulsively act them out. When we meet our children with a gentle, understanding and loving energy, without being reactionary, they will more than likely strive to make harmonious choices.

SETTING BOUNDARIES

We've talked about children craving love, connection and communication, but guess what else they actually want? Boundaries! Yes, even those kicking and screaming, red-in-the-face toddlers (or your pouty tween) want to understand what is okay with their parents and what is not. Kids feel secure when they know that their carers have boundaries in place, as this helps them feel safe in their environment.

Some examples of boundaries may be:

- It's not okay to be rough with each other's bodies.
- We only offer media on the weekend or during travel.
- We use kind words.
- We listen to each other's needs.
- We try to be helpers.

We have found that including your children in the setting of boundaries can be really helpful. Perhaps have a family meeting to talk about your values and how you can implement them in your lives. If your children are young, it can be effective to utilise a show or a character that they love to give examples of your beliefs.

> **Teresa:** My children absolutely adore Puggles, the furry creatures from Puggles and The Lost Forests (the iconic and whimsical nineties Australian toy shop that's currently having a revival). The name stands for Peace, Understanding, Generosity, Gentleness, Love and Energy, and we have incorporated these values into our family foundations. Our children know that these are the morals we believe in and they even get excited about striving to be 'more like Puggle!'

GENTLE DISCIPLINE

Naturally, all kids push boundaries and test the limits. It's one of the ways in which they grow and learn. There are many ways in which to discipline your child.

Traditional discipline, in all forms, is about attempting to control a child to get the child to conform. 'Punishments' typically stem from a place of anger, frustration, angst and fear on the part of the caregiver, and they usually have no connection to the behaviour you are wanting to correct. For example, you may take a favourite toy away for a week after your child talks back to you, or you might cancel a planned outing if your child pulls their sister's hair, but in both cases there's a disconnect between behaviour and punishment. These punishments can take a toll on your relationship with your child, and they can often be fear- and shame-inducing. Punishments take away the child's accountability for their choices.

Instead, what we choose to do is facilitate our children's learning through the cause-and-effect approach to consequences. 'Natural consequences' are favourable because they hold children responsible for their actions and help them to be mindful of the choices they make in the future. Here's an example.

SCENARIO A:

KID: 'I'm sooooo hot! I want to take my jumper off.' *tantrum*

YOU: 'You may take your jumper off, but it's very cold outside.'

kid takes jumper off

KID: 'It's freeeeeezing!'

= NATURAL CONSEQUENCE

SCENARIO B:

KID: 'I don't want dinner, I'm still playing Lego Ninjago!'

YOU: 'This is your opportunity to eat dinner. If you don't choose to eat now then you will go without dinner.'

KID: 'I said I'm playing!'

you eat your food (and probably theirs) and 8 p.m. rolls around

KID: 'I'm hungry!'

= NATURAL CONSEQUENCE

Sometimes it doesn't make sense to allow the natural consequence to unfold, such as when it could put the child in danger, when it negatively impacts someone else or if the naturally occurring consequence will be so far in the future that the child has forgotten what led to it. In this case, we can turn to a logical consequence.

Logical consequences are reasonable consequences that the caregiver comes up with. They should be directly aligned with the behaviour that you wish to address. Here's an example.

SCENARIO A:

KID: *throws toy at younger sibling for the fifth time*

YOU: 'I'm not okay with you playing rough. Your toys are for playing, not to be used as weapons. If I can't trust you to play with your toy nicely I will need to take it from you.'

KID *throws toy at brother's head*

YOU: *takes toy* 'You may have your toy back in one hour, when you can show me that you're having listening ears. I'll set a timer.'

= LOGICAL CONSEQUENCE

SCENARIO B:

KID: 'I WON'T brush my teeth, Mummy!'

YOU: 'If you don't brush then I can't give you the treats you like. We brush our teeth to keep them healthy.'

KID: 'NO!'

later, kid's sister gets an ice cream and he doesn't

YOU: 'I can't offer you an ice cream because you didn't brush your teeth.'

= LOGICAL CONSEQUENCE

When it comes to discipline, always ensure that you present a united front with your partner. Back their choices up; you don't want your child feeling confused (or worse, smug!) because their caregivers are giving contradictory directions. If you disagree with your partner's handling of something, take them aside to raise your concerns, but always show the children that you're on the same page.

THE VALUES WE TRY TO INSTIL

How do we raise mindful, earth-caring, empathetic children? We act as their mirrors! We let our actions lay the foundations of their way. If we lead with compassion and love in our daily interactions, our children will see that we are making efforts to live as mindfully as possible. This isn't to say that we won't mess up as parents, but if we aim to be our best selves, we will land closer to our intentions.

Teach your children about all the varying aspects of life. Don't be afraid to cry in front of them or to show vulnerability. Don't be afraid to ask for a 'mama do-over' if you snap at them and feel ashamed. Humanising yourself as their parent is a great way to teach them that everyone has flaws and that imperfections are a part of life. It also shows them that sadness, anger and other big feelings are transient.

BEING GLOBAL CITIZENS

We believe it's really important to teach your children that the world is massive, and that there are people living in all corners of the earth, many of whom live in very different environments from our own. Talk to them about other cultures, religions, languages and foods, as well as political beliefs and the issues of poverty and climate change. You can read books together about the ways of other lands so that your children grow up with an understanding that the world is so vast. (Faves of ours are *Welcome to Our World: A Celebration of Children Everywhere!* by Moira Butterfield and *Here We Are: Notes for Living on Planet Earth* by Oliver Jeffers.) There are always opportunities to learn from the way other people are doing things, and your kids will be so much richer knowing that everyone's experience in this world is unique, and that no one way of living trumps another.

Better yet, if your circumstances allow it, travel with your children so they can witness for themselves the array of differences. This will help them to gain awareness and, often, an appreciation of what they have and how they live. Travel doesn't need to mean flying anywhere; there's a lot to be gained from adventures that are just a train ride away! If you do decide to travel by plane, you can offset your carbon footprint by doing things like donating to forestry projects who fight the cutting down of trees while also planting new ones.

TRAVELLING WITH YOUNG KIDS

We get asked about this a lot on YZM. So many parents are worried that the moment their little one is born the days of travel and glorious vacations are over. Our jobs require us to travel, and that usually means bringing the little ones along with us. We also firmly believe that children don't stop us from doing the things we love, but rather, they make them all the more amazing because we get to share them. Sounds cheesy, but it's true. Life can be as beautiful as you want to make it; ultimately, it's all about how you approach each day and situation.

> **Sarah:** I travelled with Wyatt when he was four months old, to Mexico for Teresa's wedding. She had asked me to sing in her wedding and we were so excited to take a trip soon after Wyatt was born. This was actually pretty major for us as new parents. We had said we wanted to be people who would travel with our kids and even be spontaneous and not let having a baby hold us back. This was our first step towards accomplishing something that was important to us, and it showed us right away how rewarding and beautiful it can be to follow our instincts, even with the challenges that brings.

This all sounds nice, but how do you make the logistics work? Do you pack up a portacot, high chair, dummies, carrier, stroller and an entire package of nappies just in case? The answer is no. Less is more, and we really mean this. Travelling can be stressful, and hauling a lot of gear with you makes it even worse. Make a list of your most essential items. If you are going to stay in a hotel or rental apartment, call first and ask them a few questions.

- Do you have a crib for the room?
- Do you have a nappy service for cloth nappies?
- Are there high chairs available?
- Do you have toiletries and wipes for kids?
- Do you provide a nanny service?
- Do you have a stroller for loan, or a car seat?

Doing this will give you a better idea of what you will need to bring with you. Depending on where you are travelling, you may only need a carrier, not a stroller. Here is a travel checklist you can add to or use as a base.

- Toy or blankie that your little one loves
- Dummy (bring a few because you will most likely drop them on the plane)
- Hand sanitiser to wipe down armrests and food trays
- Children's fever reducer such as Panadol
- Clothes – bring lots of options. These are probably the most important, because you never know when you will have a blowout or may need a jumper if the weather turns.
- Pack an extra shirt for yourself in your nappy bag or backpack. This will be a saving grace in the event of an accidental poo explosion or vomit.
- Carrier
- A scooter bag for the older kids to zip around the airport on and have their stuff in (sooo handy!)
- Disposable and cloth nappies plus wipes – and a rubbish bag
- A bento box of snacks for you and your little one
- A few toys to entertain your child in-flight (some people like to bring

- something new for their little ones to keep them entertained for longer)
- Colouring books and crayons
- Swaddle blanket to lay on the floor if you want to put your little one down to play at the airport or hotel
- A small child's neck pillow

Sarah: Personally, I've never loved bringing a stroller with me – I love using a carrier and a backpack for my travels. When Wyatt was around three I got a ride-on suitcase for him so I could pull him while carrying my daughter in the carrier. The ride-on suitcase held his clothes plus some toys and snacks, and I could carry all the things for the baby in my backpack. I like packing and travelling light because it means I have less to keep up with and worry about.

Things can happen while travelling that make life feel a bit more complicated. Babies don't understand what is happening when the pressure in their ears builds up on take-off and landing, so make sure you give them a dummy, your thumb to suck on or breastfeed or bottle-feed them during that time. If you time it right (this does happen – occasionally!) your little one will fall asleep while nursing during take-off, giving you some extra time to slip on some headphones and watch half a movie. Some babies may feel restless and need a bit of rocking or walking while in flight. As with anything, just watch their cues and know that this is very new for your baby, so try to help them.

Sarah: I had a friend who was very organised, and when taking her little one on his first flight she made a little bag for everyone in the small cabin that said 'Hi! This is my first flight, please be patient with me.' Inside the bag was a pair of earplugs. I thought this was adorable and probably made mum feel more supported and less worried about the idea of her little one crying during the flight.

Sleep patterns may change during travel – this is hard to avoid. Try not to stress about your little one going to bed at the wrong time or missing their nap. They will sleep and get back on track eventually, and the best thing you can do is be there to assist them and comfort them. There are lots of tips and tricks to getting young kids onto a different time zone, but we don't want you to feel defeated if they don't work for you. It may work best to have them try to sleep when you sleep. That way if they wake up in the middle of the night you can remind them that it's still dark outside. Try to keep your voice low and the lights off and help them to sleep. This won't always work – you may have a party in your bed in the middle of the night – but after a few days you will find your rhythm.

We try to approach travel like anything else in life: we come at it with joy, try to be prepared and accept that not everything will go as planned. At the end of the day, you *will* get there, your little one will eventually sleep and you will get to show them a whole new experience or culture. Ultimately, they will become more adaptable humans because of the adventure.

Sarah: When Wyatt was ten months old we flew to Portugal for my brother-in-law's wedding. We decided to hit up an island in Italy first, so we had to fly from LAX to London to Rome, then travel from Rome to Naples by train and from Naples to the island of Ischia by boat. We had one night to sleep in Rome to break it up a bit, but even so, with a ten-month-old this was a very adventurous endeavour! When we got on the plane in Los Angeles all seemed good, and we felt excited and prepared. But an hour into our flight Wyatt started to feel hot. His temperature was 39°C. I panicked – this was an eight-hour flight and I had nothing to reduce his fever. I spoke to the flight attendant and thankfully they had some children's Panadol. I lay next to him the whole flight monitoring his temp, keeping him hydrated with milk and falling in and out of sleep. This was a big lesson for me, and now I always bring a few important medicines, just in case. Thankfully the fever was gone the next day and we continued on our journey, which went smoothly.

SLOWING DOWN AND UNPLUGGING

Our fast-paced society can present many issues. The boom of technology means we have access to many things we once didn't. Consumerism is an epidemic, and much of it is aimed at children and parents. Too many stimuli and too much stuff means we are neglecting the ways of the past, when we'd open the back door and let our kids run in the fields for hours, making their own fun with each other.

We want the very best for them, so we sign up for *all* the activities, jam-packing their days with adventures and experiences, thinking we are doing what's best for them. But nowadays our kids are wildly overscheduled: tennis lessons, rock climbing, piano, surf club, maths group, chess, ballet . . . the list is endless. No wonder we feel like life is flying past us. It's manic and rushed, and, if we're honest, this busyness is self-imposed. How often do you find yourself feeling frazzled, rushed or stressed out? Probably more often than you'd like.

Let's talk about changing our ways. It is simple really: we slow down. We become comfortable breaking up with 'yes' (yes we'll attend that party, yes we'll carpool to soccer, yes we'll host the school dinner . . .). By doing that, we are in fact saying yes to ourselves. Try to keep the family schedule in check so that each member has time to restore, relax and connect with themselves and each other (preferably in a technology-free environment). This brings balance back into the home.

As an exercise, try to incorporate at least one day a week where you have zero plans. This gives you a free day when kids and adults can do as they please, no pressure, no expectations; you just get to be. We try to do this as much as possible, and those rare free days end up being some of our favourite days. They feel long, lazy and connected. Stripped of frenzied activity. Less technology, less stuff, just human interaction, imagination and freedom. We feel like we have room to breathe. It's a lovely way to recharge before getting back to the grind.

CHOICES FOR YOUR LITTLE ONE'S FUTURE

Our children learn by watching us, so while we are trying to figure out how we want to parent, it is also important to look inside. Look at yourself and the world around you. What can you teach through your own action? It is amazing how much your child will pick up on – those little things can make a big impact.

We live in a time where the choices we make directly affect the world we live in. Our generation and the ones that follow are waking up and demanding change, because there is no way to deny what we are seeing all over our planet. Just recently our children marched in the climate strike led by young activist Greta Thunberg, and we marched proudly alongside them with their homemade signs and demands for action.

Our kids see our choice to bring a reusable cup to the coffee shop, to compost our food scraps, to recycle our garbage, to say no to plastic straws and question restaurants that still offer them. Our very young children will challenge us as they grow up in a world where big brands make important strides to reduce waste by making clothes and shoes out of recycled water bottles and plastics.

The two of us did not grow up with this awareness. For us, and many others, plastic bags, single-use plastics, excess food waste and overconsumption of meat products was pretty normal. We've had to learn, make major changes to our lives and break habits that once felt very natural and normal.

If we teach our children to be eco warriors, environmentalists and keepers of the planet at a very young age, this will be normal for them. They will understand what it means to sort, recycle and compost their garbage, to use less, consume less, to drive hybrid and electric cars. They will challenge the people around them to be kind to our planet and animals. They will grow up to start companies built on eco-conscious values, and they will always ask the question, 'What more can we do?'

If this all sounds a little overwhelming, don't worry! We have some practical tips for small changes you can make in your home that will in turn make a big impact on the planet and your little one's future.

> **Sarah:** I grew up in Kentucky in a small farming town. Meat was a part of almost every meal and it was very normal to us. When our son was three, we made a choice as a family to give up meat products, only eat a little fish and live a more 'vegetarian' lifestyle. Wyatt was pretty sad about it as he loved meat and he loves food in general. But we called it our new family adventure and we explained how what we eat and how often we eat it makes a huge impact on our planet. We said we would try this adventure and see how it goes, letting him know that if he wanted to have meat (from a good source) he could and has on a few occasions and that is his choice. It's been three years and we are all still very happy with our adventure.

This might feel drastic for some people, but if you are a big meat eater don't fret: you can actually make a huge impact by taking meat out of your day once a week. Here are some tips to help you through your family eco journey.

- Meatless Monday. Want to know the impact of taking meat out of your diet one day a week? Food production is major contributor to greenhouse gas emissions in Australia, and roughly 70 per cent of emissions caused by agriculture in Australia come from livestock. [3]
- Say no to plastic straws and cutlery.
- Challenge restaurants that offer these and ask them to make changes. Use alternatives made from bamboo, metal, glass, pasta and more.
- No more plastic water bottles or bags.
- Bring your own canteen with you, store one in your car and send your kids to school with refillable water bottles.
- Plastic bags end up in oceans and landfills. Bring your own bags with you –

a great tip is to carry them in your car so you don't have to remember them when you leave the house.

- Food waste. Composting could reduce emissions by 2.3 billion tons over the next 30 years. [4] In some places, you can put your food scraps in your green waste bin and your council will compost them for you. You can also get small compost bins to keep in your yard or on your balcony, and use the soil created to nourish your plants and garden.

- Ditch the car. If you can, ride your bike or take public transport rather than using a car. Road transport currently accounts for 15 per cent of all greenhouse gas emissions in Australia, but a full bus can take 40 cars off the road and a full passenger train more than 500 cars. [5] If you can't avoid driving a car, consider choosing a hybrid or electric car instead.

- Reduce your water waste. Take shorter showers, or shower with your little ones.

- Save energy. Use energy efficient light bulbs, turn off lights when they aren't needed and unplug electronics that are not in use.

- Spend consciously.

- Buy from companies that are making changes and building businesses to aid planet conservation. Make sure you are buying ocean and eco-friendly sunscreens, and chemical-free products that use alternatives to plastics or recycled plastic.

- Support nonprofits that are working to make changes, and join or create a green committee at your child's preschool or school to help teach the students to be waste-free forward thinkers.

Reuse. Donate unwanted clothes and toys to organisations that will give them to families in need. Ask your friends for hand-me-downs for your kids to reduce spending and clothes production.

You don't have to do all of these things, but making small changes in your home will help teach your children the importance of taking care of our planet and will reduce your footprint. Encourage your little ones to come up with ideas of things that you can do as a family, then write a list and have everyone in the family sign it. You can say this is our family adventure and we are in this together. Tell your kids to remind you if they ever see you forgetting something on the list. This will empower your children and give them responsibility. This is how we teach our children through our own actions and mistakes.

THE STORY CONTINUES

As with our own journeys attempting to live Zen(ish), conscious, love-filled lives, this story of motherhood continues – the learning never stops. Don't be fooled by the beautiful, ethereal, sun-kissed photos in this book; like you, our days are filled with constant negotiation, work, self-reflection, stress, tantrums, messes and mistakes.

We hope you will continue your journey of knowledge and share a common desire to teach our children through communication, love and an ability to adapt so we can grow our babies into empathetic thoughtful kids, teens and adults. Our world needs parents like you to nurture the next generation of open-minded and thoughtful children. Our planet needs kids to understand its beauty and the importance of maintaining it.

Through our blog and all our most-loved resources, we hope you are able to find the answers to your questions as the days, weeks and years roll on. Just know that we are here with you, raising our kids, learning from our peers and navigating alongside you throughout the hardest and most rewarding job that exists.

YOUR ZEN MAMA RESOURCE GUIDE

PODCASTS

Australian Birth Stories

Dr Berlin's Informed Pregnancy
Podcast

The Birth Hour

Rockstar Birth

The Mother Loving Future

Janet Lansbury's Unruffled

Atomic Moms

Oprah's Super Soul Conversations

BOOKS

Spiritual Midwifery by Ina May Gaskin

Ina May's Guide to Childbirth by Ina
May Gaskin

Ina May's Guide to Breastfeeding by Ina
May Gaskin

Birth Matters by Ina May Gaskin

The Continuum Concept by Jean
Liedloff

The Baby Book by Dr William Sears

The Attachment Parenting Book by Dr
William Sears

Buddhism for Mothers by Sarah
Napthali

*The Mama Natural Week-by-Week
Guide to Pregnancy and Childbirth*
by Genevieve Howland

The First Forty Days by Amely
Greevan, Heng Ou and Marisa
Belger

No Bad Kids by Janet Lansbury

Play the Forest School Way by Peter
Houghton and Jane Worrell

The Conscious Parent by Dr Shefali
Tsabary

The Womanly Art of Breastfeeding

Permission to Parent by Robin Berman,
MD

Up the Duff by Kaz Cooke

Pregnancy Childbirth and the Newborn
by Penny Simkin, Janet Whalley,
Janelle Durham and April Bolding

The Sleepeasy Solution by Jennifer
Waldburger and Jill Spivack

The Kindness Advantage by Dale Atkins
and Amanda Salzhauer

The Happiest Baby on the Block by
Harvey Karp, MD

WEBSITES

mamanatural.com

mamamia.com.au

mysticmamma.com

inamay.com

janetlansbury.com

ohsheglows.com

birthwithoutfearblog.com

every-mother.com

gozen.com

binibirth.com

happiestbaby.com.au

spinningbabies.com

SOCIAL MEDIA
ACCOUNTS

Australianbirthstories

Birthofamama

Badassmotherbirther

Mandaliabirth

Thebirthstories

Carriagehousebirth

Themotherlovingfuture

Mamamiaparents

Mamanatural

Yourzenmama (duh!)

Gemma_peanut

DOCUMENTARIES

*Birth Story: Ina May Gaskin and The
    Farm Midwives*

The Business of Being Born

*Misunderstandings of Miscarriage
    (M.O.M.)*

ACKNOWLEDGEMENTS

To our children: Wyatt, Bodhi, Esmé, Forest, Poet & Isaac (and the others to follow!). You made us mothers and ignited the passion in us for all we share in this book. We love you endlessly; you are our greatest joys, and our most insightful teachers. Thank you.

To our husbands Eric and Mark. Thank you for the hours we were able to disappear and take time to write, research, focus, eat ice cream, drink wine and dream our book into existence. Your partnership, love and support gave us the courage and freedom to take on what sometimes seemed to be a large and terrifying task. We should probably take this moment to let you know that our next dream is to live commune-style as one giant family.

To our mothers and grandmothers; we know love because you showed us love first. This gave us the confidence to share our hearts with the world. Thank you for showing us the way – Debbie, Paula, Kaaren, Dora, Levon, Barbara and Jeanne.

To Sonya Bishop, Kacy Byxbee, Morrin O'Shea, Alex Conti-Lewis, Deb Harkness, Claire Hoban, Anna Schafer, Kevin Palmer, Kate Dyfan, Chrissy Duigan, Kate Clarke and Kathryn Mason. Thank you for being our people; your love, guidance and support in all its forms enabled us to take on this passion project.

A huge thank you to our commissioning editor, Isabelle Yates, our editors Fay Helfenbaum and Vanessa Lanaway, and to Penguin Random House Australia for asking us to write this book and encouraging us when doubt and vulnerability crept in.

Thanks to our talented designer Louisa Maggio, Kate Dyfan for your stunning illustrations of the female body, Gemma Pranita for capturing our world with your lens and Cassandra Kerr for navigating all the permissions and being our logistics hero.

To our whole Your Zen Mama community: we could not have done this without you. You have inspired us to write about the subjects that we love most and you have shown us the way through your raw and heartfelt contributions to yourzenmama.com

To our generous contributors, your time and words are so valuable. We can't express our gratitude enough for sharing them with us; your impact on this book is moving, insightful and nurturing. Thank you to Ana Paula Markel, Julie Schiller, Dr Elliot Berlin and Dr Alyssa Berlin, Karine Williams, Megan Gale, Gemma Pranita, Maria Harpas, Aida Garcia Toledo, Tahyna MacManus, Maggie Howell, Michelle Kenway, Suzanne Swan, Dr William Sears, Dr Harvey Karp, Professor James McKenna, Dr Darcia Narvaez, Sharifa Oppenheimer, Tammy Obst and everyone who gave their professional contribution towards our book.

ENDNOTES

CHAPTER 1

1. Mena, G. P., Mielke, G. I. and Brown,
W. J., 'The Effect of Physical Activity on
Reproductive Health Outcomes in Young
Women: A Systematic Review and Meta-
analysis', *Human Reproduction Update*, vol.
25, no. 5, 2019, pp. 542—564

2. Genea, 'How to increase sperm count',
Genea [website], 2019, https://www.genea.
com.au/natural-conception/male-fertility,
(accessed 21 November 2019)

CHAPTER 2

1. Pregnancy, Birth & Baby, 'Miscarriage',
Pregnancy, Birth & Baby [website], 2019,
pregnancybirthbaby.org.au, (accessed 21
November 2019)

2. Hure, A. J. et al., 'Miscarriage, Preterm
Delivery, and Stillbirth: Large Variations
in Rates within a Cohort of Australian
Women', *PLoS* ONE, vol. 7, no. 5, https://
doi.org/10.1371/journal.pone.0037109,
(accessed 21 November 2019)

3. The Women's, 'Miscarriage', *The Royal
Women's Hospital* [website], 2019, https://
www.thewomens.org.au/health-information/
pregnancy-and-birth/pregnancy-problems/
early-pregnancy-problems/miscarriage,
(accessed 21 November 2019)

4. Pregnancy, Birth & Baby, 'Miscarriage',
Pregnancy, Birth & Baby [website], 2019,
https://www.pregnancybirthbaby.org.au/
miscarriage, (accessed 21 November 2019)

5. Parents, 'Preventing Miscarriage: Is
There Anything You Can Do?', *Parents*
[website], 2019, https://www.parents.com/
pregnancy/complications/miscarriage/
preventing-miscarriage-is-there-anything-
you-can-do/, (accessed 21 November 2019)

6. Li, Y. H. and Marren, A., 'Recurrent
Pregnancy Loss: A Summary of International
Evidence-based Guidelines and Practice',
Australian Journal of General Practice, vol. 47,
no. 7, https://www1.racgp.org.au/ajgp/2018/
july/recurrent-pregnancy-loss/, (accessed 21
November 2019)

7. Australian Institute of Health and
Welfare, *Stillbirths and Neonatal Deaths in
Australia*: 2015 and 2016, 2019, https://
www.aihw.gov.au/reports/mothers-
babies/stillbirths-neonatal-deaths-
australia-2015-2016/report-editions,
(accessed 21 November 2019)

8. Australian Institute of Health and
Welfare, *Stillbirths and Neonatal Deaths in
Australia*: 2015 and 2016, 2019, https://
www.aihw.gov.au/reports/mothers-
babies/stillbirths-neonatal-deaths-

9. Australian Institute of Health and Welfare, *Stillbirths and Neonatal Deaths in Australia*: 2015 and 2016, 2019, https://www.aihw.gov.au/reports/mothers-babies/stillbirths-neonatal-deaths-australia-2015-2016/report-editions

10. Stillbirth Foundation Australia, 'Prevention', 2019, *Stillbirth Foundation Australia* [website], https://stillbirthfoundation.org.au/prevention/, (accessed 21 November 2109)

11. The Women's, 'After a Miscarriage', *The Royal Women's Hospital* [website], 2017, https://www.thewomens.org.au/images/uploads/fact-sheets/After-miscarriage-090419.pdf, (accessed 21 November 2019)

12. Sunderman A. C. et al, 'Interpregnancy Interval After Pregnancy Loss and Risk of Repeat Miscarriage', *Obstet Gynecol.*, vol. 130, no. 6, 2017, pp.1312–1318

CHAPTER 3

1. Tong, S. et al, 'Miscarriage Risk for Asymptomatic Women After a Normal First-Trimester Prenatal Visit', *Obstetrics & Gynecology*, vol. 111, no. 3, 2008, pp. 710–714

2. de Seymour, J. V. et al, 'Omega-3 supplements in pregnancy reduce the risk of premature birth', *Nutrition Journal*, vol. 18, no. 74, 2019, https://doi.org/10.1186/s12937-019-0499-2, (accessed 26 November 2019)

3. Victoria State Government, 'Food Poisoning – Listeria', *Better Health Channel* [website], 2018, https://www.betterhealth.vic.gov.au/health/healthyliving/food-poisoning-listeria, (accessed 26 November 2019)

4. Chen, M. et al, 'Residential Exposure to Pesticide During Childhood and Childhood Cancers: A Meta-Analysis', *Pediatrics*, vol. 144, no. 5, 2015, https://doi.org/10.1542/peds.2015-0006, (accessed 26 November 2019)

5. Pregnancy, Birth & Baby, 'Toxic Household Products to Avoid During Pregnancy', *Pregnancy, Birth & Baby* [website], 2018, https://www.pregnancybirthbaby.org.au/toxic-household-products-to-avoid-during-pregnancy, (accessed 26 November 2019)

6. Pregnancy, Birth & Baby, 'Morning Sickness', *Pregnancy, Birth & Baby* [website], 2018, https://www.pregnancybirthbaby.org.au/dealing-with-morning-sickness, (accessed 26 November 2019)

7. McCulloch, S., 'How Much Does it Cost to Give Birth in Australia?', *BellyBelly.com.au* [website], 2018, https://www.bellybelly.com.au/birth/how-much-does-it-cost-to-give-birth-in-australia/, (accessed 26 November 2019)

CHAPTER 4

1. Declercq E. R. et al, *Listening to Mothers*[SM] *III: Pregnancy and Birth*, 2013, www. nationalpartnership.org/listeningtomothers, (accessed 3 Dec 2019)

2. Mater Mothers' Hospital, 'Labour and birth—warm water immersion and water birth', *Mater Mothers' Hospital* [website], 2017, http://brochures.mater.org.au/ brochures/mater-mothers-hospital/labour- and-birth-warm-water-immersion-and- water-bi, (accessed 3 December 2019)

3. Australian Institute of Health and Welfare, *Australia's Health 2018: In Brief*, 2018, https://www.aihw.gov.au/reports/ australias-health/australias-health-2018-in- brief/contents/births-in-australia, (accessed 3 December 2019)

CHAPTER 6

1. Hoekzema, E. et al, 'Pregnancy leads to long-lasting changes in human brain structure', *Nature Neuroscience*, vol. 20, 2017, https://www.nature.com/articles/ nn.4458, (accessed 3 December 2019)

2. Mayo Clinic Staff, 'Postpartum Depression', *Mayo Clinic* [website], 2018, https://www.mayoclinic.org/diseases- conditions/postpartum-depression/ symptoms-causes/syc-20376617, (accessed 3 December 2019)

3. BabyCenter editorial team, 'How Can I Find a Doula to Attend My Birth?', *BabyCenter* [website], 2019, https://www. babycenter.com.au/x2445/how-can-i-find- a-doula-to-attend-my-birth, (accessed 3 December 2019)

CHAPTER 7

1. del Castillo-Hegyi, C., 'The Scientific Evidence on the Effects of Underfeeding on the Newborn Brain: A Review of the Literature', *Fed is Best* [website], 2016, https://fedisbest.org/2016/09/the- scientific-evidence-on-the-effects-on- accidental-starvation-on-the-newborn- brain/, (accessed 3 December 2019)

2. La Leche League GB, 'Dummies and Breastfeeding', *La Leche League GB* [website], 2019, https://www.laleche.org.uk/ dummies-and-breastfeeding/, (accessed 3 December 2019)

3. Raising Children, 'Baby Carriers, Slings and Backpacks: Safety Guide', *Raising Children* [website], https://raisingchildren. net.au/newborns/safety/equipment- furniture/baby-carrier-sling-safety, (accessed 3 December 2019)

4. Moon, R. Y., 'SIDS and Other Sleep- Related Infant Deaths: Evidence Base for 2016 Updated Recommendations for a Safe Infant Sleeping Environment', *Pediatrics*, vol. 138, no. 5, 2016, https://pediatrics. aappublications.org/content/138/5/ e20162940, (accessed 3 December 2019)

5. Haelle, T., 'New Guidelines Acknowledge The Reality: Babies Do Sleep In Mom's Bed', *NPR* [website],

2016, https://www.npr.org/sections/
health-shots/2016/10/25/499290404/
new-guidelines-acknowledge-the-reality-
babies-do-sleep-in-moms-bed, (accessed 3
December 2019)

6. McKenna, J. J., 'Cosleeping and Biological
Imperatives: Why Human Babies Do Not and
Should Not Sleep Alone', *Neuroanthropology*
[website], 2008, https://neuroanthropology.
net/2008/12/21/cosleeping-and-biological-
imperatives-why-human-babies-do-not-
and-should-not-sleep-alone/, (accessed 3
December 2019)

7. University of Notre Dame, 'Safe
Cosleeping Guidelines', *Mother–Baby
Behavioral Sleep Laboratory* [website], 2019,
https://cosleeping.nd.edu/safe-co-sleeping-
guidelines/, (accessed 3 December 2019)

8. Schön, R. A., & Silvén, M., 'Natural
Parenting – Back to Basics in Infant Care',
Evolutionary Psychology, 2007, https://
doi.org/10.1177/147470490700500110,
(accessed 3 December 2019)

CHAPTER 8

1. Dingfelder, S., 'Must Babies Always
Breed Marital Discontent?', *American
Psychological Association*, vol. 2 no. 9, 2011,
https://www.apa.org/monitor/2011/10/
babies, (accessed 3 December 2019)

2. Kwan, C., 'Why Are More and More
Australian Mums Starting Their Own
Business?', *Collective Hub* [website], 2017,
https://collectivehub.com/2017/12/why-are-
more-and-more-australian-mums-starting-

their-own-business/, (accessed
3 December 2019)

3. Department of Primary Industries and
Regional Development, 'Reducing Livestock
Greenhouse Gas Emissions', *Agriculture
and Food* [website], 2019, https://www.
agric.wa.gov.au/climate-change/reducing-
livestock-greenhouse-gas-emissions,
(accessed 3 December 2019)

4. Habits of Waste, 'Food Waste', *Habits
of Waste.org* [website], http://www.
habitsofwaste.org/call-to-action/food-
waste/, (accessed 3 December 2019)

5. OzEBus, 'Climate Change and Public
Transport', *OzEBus* [website], http://bic.asn.
au/information-for-moving-people/climate-
change-and-public-transport, (accessed 3
December 2019)

EBURY PRESS

UK | USA | Canada | Ireland | Australia
India | New Zealand | South Africa | China

Ebury Press is part of the Penguin Random House group of companies
whose addresses can be found at global.penguinrandomhouse.com.

Penguin
Random House
Australia

First published by Ebury Press, 2020

Cover photography by Gemma Pranita
Cover design by Louisa Maggio © Penguin Random House Australia Pty Ltd
Text design by Louisa Maggio © Penguin Random House Australia Pty Ltd
Illustrations by Kate Dyfan
All photographs by Gemma Pranita except p34 (Stuart Kerr), p55 (Melissa Jean, @melissajeanbabies),
p58 (Tyler William Parker), p101 (Mark Webber), p107 (Eric Olsen), p139 (Teresa Palmer)
Photo collage (top to bottom, left to right):
Morrin O'Shea, Teresa Palmer, Carlos Ulloa, Sonya Bishop, Sarah Wright Olsen.
Teresa Palmer, Mark Webber, Teresa Palmer, Annabelle Harron, Teresa Palmer, Claire Hoban.
Sarah Wright Olsen, Teresa Palmer, Jenny Tunberg.
Mark Webber, Jenny Tunberg, Sarah Wright Olsen, Sarah Wright Olsen, Claire Hoban.

Internal design by Louisa Maggio

Printed and bound in China by RR Donnelley Asia Printing Solutions Limited Ltd

A catalogue record for this
book is available from the
National Library of Australia

ISBN 978 1 76089 280 7

penguin.com.au